TEACHER'S RESOURCE

BLACKLINE MASTERS AND TEACHER'S MANUAL

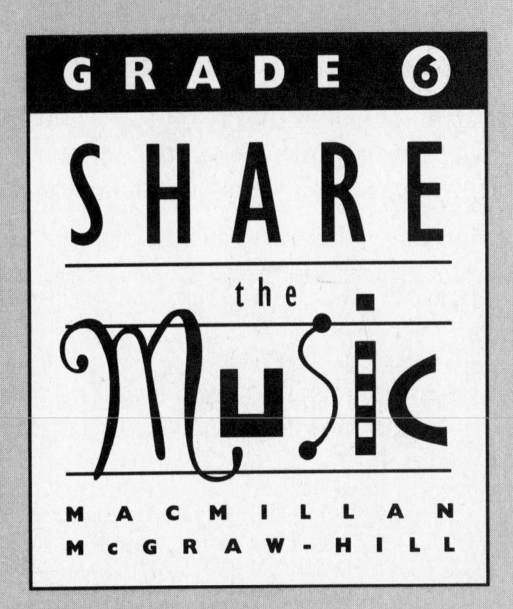

SERIES AUTHORS

Judy Bond
Coordinating Author

René Boyer-White

Margaret Campbelle-duGard

Marilyn Copeland Davidson
Coordinating Author

Robert de Frece

Mary Goetze
Coordinating Author

Doug Goodkin

Betsy M. Henderson

Michael Jothen

Carol King

Vincent P. Lawrence
Coordinating Author

Nancy L. T. Miller

Ivy Rawlins

Susan Snyder
Coordinating Author

Macmillan/McGraw-Hill School Publishing Company
New York • Columbus

INTRODUCTION

This ***Teacher's Resource Masters*** book contains supplementary activities for ***Share the Music.***

The Resource Masters include the following:

- A variety of activities that reinforce or review concepts taught in the lessons. Some Resource Masters emphasize manipulative activities, while others offer written and aural activities.
- Listening maps that provide visual guidance for students as they listen to specific music selections. The listening maps help students identify melodic and rhythmic patterns, tone color, form, and other musical elements.
- Assessment questions for each unit. The assessment questions and music examples are recorded. Two recorded options are available for each question.
- Scripts for musicals.
- Tools for Assessment, including portfolio and self-assessment forms.
- An answer key.

All Resource Masters may be duplicated for classroom use. Each is keyed into the Teacher's Edition. A line at the bottom of the Resource Master identifies the page in the Teacher's Edition with which the Resource Master is intended to be used.

For listening maps, teaching suggestions are provided on the back of the Resource Master.

Macmillan/McGraw-Hill School Division
10 Union Square East
New York, New York 10003

Printed in the United States of America

ISBN 0-02-295091-5 / 6/8

2 3 4 5 6 7 8 9 MAL 99 98 97 96 95 94

Table of Contents

Name ____________________

The Music Makers Chart

Chart your favorite musical groups. Tell the name of the group, the instruments used, and interesting facts about the group. Each time you listen to a recording or go to a concert, add the group to your chart.

The Music Makers Chart

Group	Instruments	Comments

My favorite group was ____________________

because ____________________

____

____

Name ____________________

RESOURCE MASTER 1•2 Practice

The Four Instrument Families

Write the instrument name below each picture. Then name the instrument family (woodwind, brass, percussion, string).

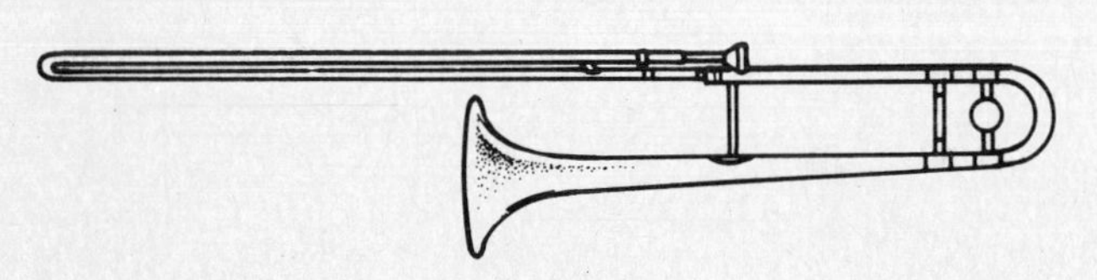

1. ____________________

____

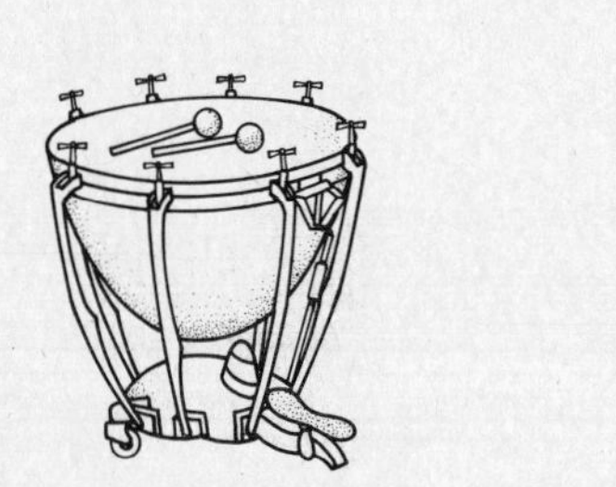

2. ____________________

____

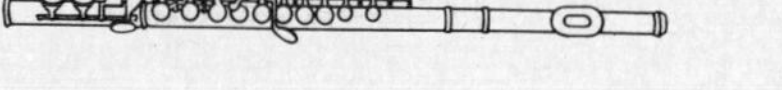

3. ____________________

____

4. ____________________

____

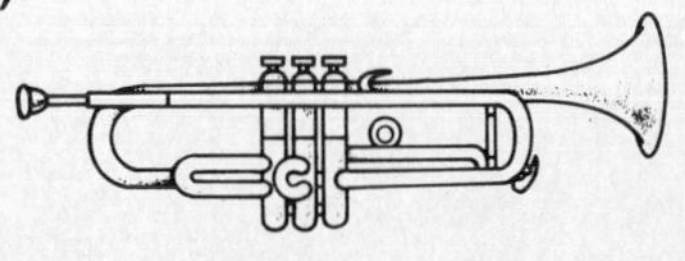

5. ____________________

____

6. ____________________

____

7. ____________________

____

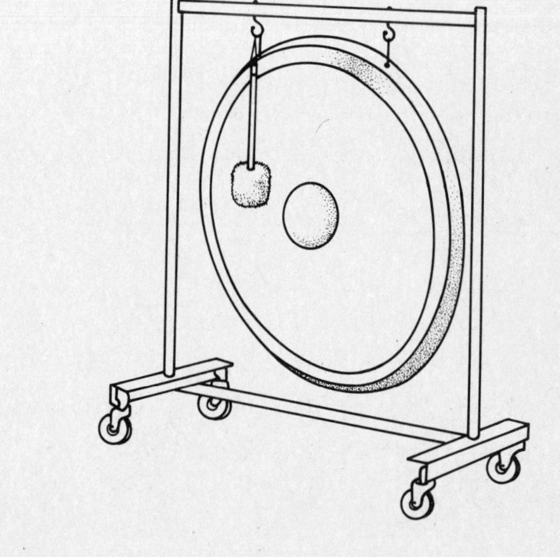

8. ____________________

____

Name ______________________________

Pop Music Pros: Johnny Mercer and Harold Arlen

There is hardly an American alive who hasn't heard at least one song by Johnny Mercer (1909–1976) or Harold Arlen (1905–1986). Their songs are some of the longest-lasting of American pop music. Mercer wrote or co-wrote more than a thousand songs including "Moon River" and "Jeepers Creepers." Arlen wrote more than five hundred songs, including "Over the Rainbow" and "Stormy Weather." Both men won many awards.

When they wrote songs together, Mercer wrote the lyrics and Arlen wrote the music. Most of their songs were written for films. "Accentuate the Positive" was written for *Here Come the Waves*, a movie about women in the World War II Navy. The two also wrote "That Old Black Magic," and "Blues in the Night," smash hits in the 30s and 40s.

"Accentuate the Positive"
by Mercer/Arlen

Mercer was born in Savannah, Georgia. Although he is most famous as a lyricist, he also sang on many records and on his own radio show. Mercer was as successful at business as he was at music—he was one of the founders of Capitol Records, a large record company.

Arlen, who got his start singing in a synagogue choir in his hometown of Buffalo, New York, got his first big break writing songs for Harlem's famous Cotton Club singers in the 1930s. Some of the songs he wrote for the Cotton Club were "I Love a Parade" and "Stormy Weather." Arlen also continued to perform. In fact, the recording he made of "Stormy Weather" became a hit even before it was sung at the Cotton Club.

Arlen also wrote many scores for movies and Broadway musicals. He wrote several of the numbers for *The Wizard of Oz*, including "Over the Rainbow" (lyrics by E.Y. Harburg), which made singer Judy Garland a star and won a 1939 Academy Award. The movie company almost didn't put the song in the movie, believing it was too sophisticated for children, the movie's intended audience.

Name ____________________

RESOURCE MASTER 1•3 Background

Page 2

Use the clues to complete the puzzle.

ACROSS

1 A hit song that Arlen recorded himself
6 The person who writes the words of a song
7 Mercer co-founded a large ______ company.
9 When Mercer and Arlen worked together, Arlen wrote this part of the song.
10 Arlen's first name
14 "________ the Positive"
16 Mercer wrote more than 1000; Arlen wrote more than 500.
17 A tune, a pleasing combination of sounds; a musical element
18 Mercer and Arlen often wrote songs for ________.
19 A show or play made up of songs, dances, and spoken dialogue

DOWN

1 Birthplace of Johnny Mercer
2 Famous Arlen/Harburg song
3 Worked with Harold Arlen
4 Arlen and Mercer both ________ many awards.
5 Person who plays a role in a movie or a play
8 A type of pop music; rock 'n' __________
11 Their invention made it possible for a singer to be heard across the country.
12 Playing this girl made Judy Garland a star.
13 *Here Come the* ________
15 The key signature of a song ________ you what pitch is do.

Name ________________________________

Drum Playalong: "National Emblem"

A Play 4 times

B 𝄋

D.S. 𝄋 Trio 𝄌

D.S. 𝄌

1. 2.

Name ______________________________

RESOURCE MASTER 1•5 Practice

Rhythm Roundup

In the box below, write these notes in order from longest to shortest duration: half note, quarter note, whole note, eighth note.

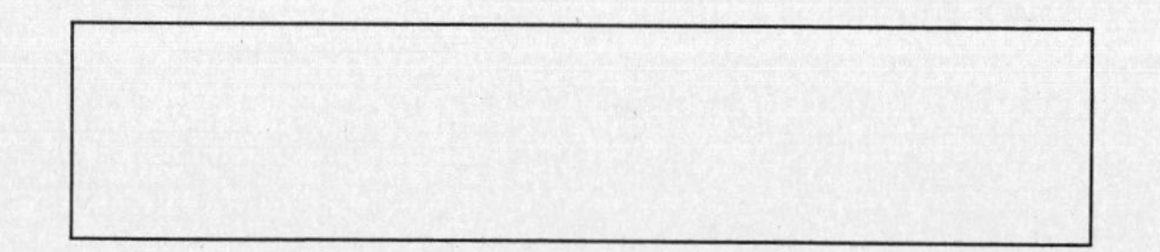

Study the note values below. Circle the example in each pair that has more beats than the other example.

1. a. ♩ ♩ b. ♫
2. a. 𝅝 b. ♩ ♩
3. a. ♩ ♩ ♩ b. 𝅝
4. a. ♩ b. ♪
5. a. 𝅝 b. 𝅗𝅥
6. a. ♩ ♩ ♩ b. 𝅗𝅥
7. a. ♩ ♫ b. 𝅝
8. a. 𝅗𝅥 ♩ b. 𝅝
9. a. ♫ b. 𝅗𝅥
10. a. 𝅝 b. ♩
11. a. ♩ ♫ b. ♪
12. a. 𝅗𝅥 ♫ b. 𝅝
13. a. 𝅗𝅥 𝅗𝅥 b. ♫ ♩
14. a. 𝅝 b. ♩ 𝅗𝅥
15. a. ♫ 𝅗𝅥 b. ♩ ♩ 𝅗𝅥
16. a. ♫ ♫ b. ♩

Name ____

Sherlock Tones: The Case of the Empty Case

London's most famous music professor Dr. Piccolo cannot find his valuable violin. Has he misplaced it or was it stolen? Dr. Piccolo calls the famous detective Sherlock Tones. Help Tones solve the mystery by decoding the musical clues below.

Write the pitch letter names on the lines below the staff to find the musical clues. Then play the examples on pitched instruments.

1. CLUES

repairs ___ ___ ___ ___ ___

2.

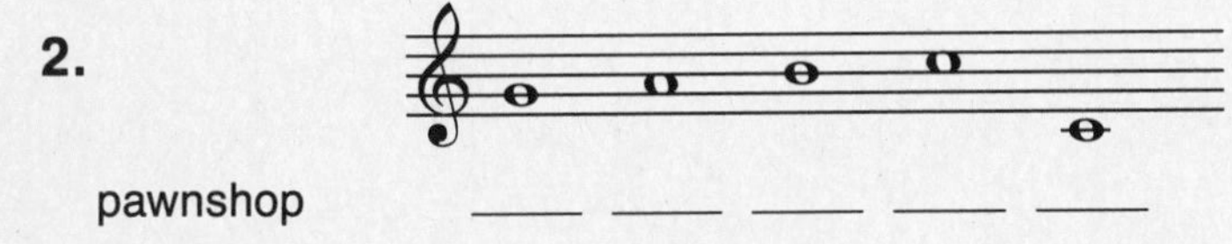

pawnshop ___ ___ ___ ___ ___

3.

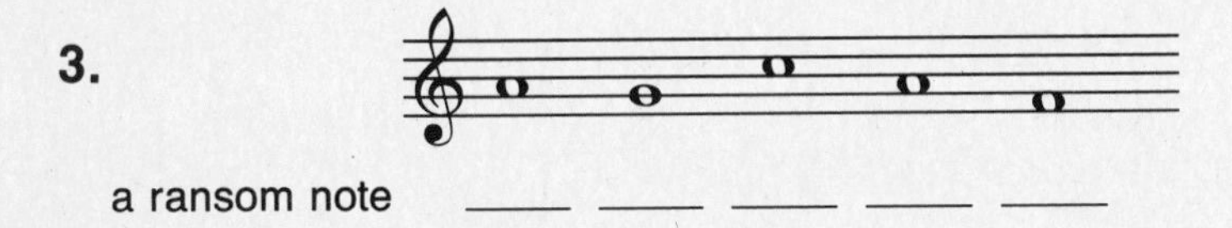

a ransom note ___ ___ ___ ___ ___

4.

borrowed ___ ___ ___ ___ ___

5.

fingerprints ___ ___ ___ ___ ___

6.

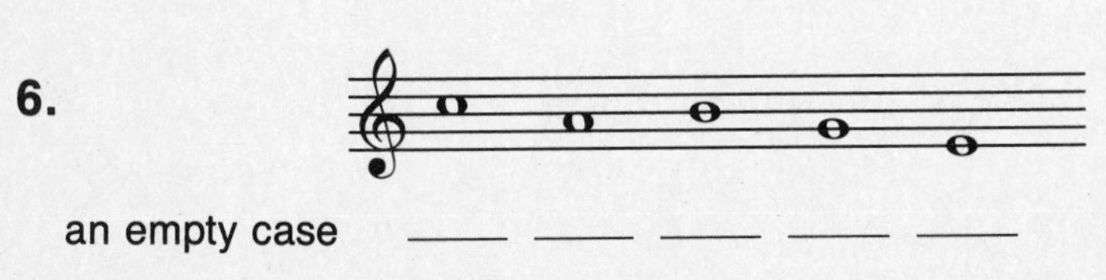

an empty case ___ ___ ___ ___ ___

Use page 2 to solve the case.

Name ______________________________

RESOURCE MASTER 1•6

Page 2

Under the blanks below are the answers to the exercises on page 1. Find the notation on page 1 that matches the pitch letter names below each blank. Next to the notation is a clue. Write the clue in the blank to help Sherlock Tones solve the case of the missing violin.

Tones went to the vault where Dr. Piccolo kept his violin.

There Tones found **(7.)** ____________________.
C' A B G E

Thinking the violin might be stolen, Tones checked but found

no **(8.)** ____________________. "If the violin were stolen,"
G F D E A

said Tones, "then we would have received **(9.)** ____________
A G C' A F

by now. Or perhaps the thief did not know its value and sold

it at a **(10.)** ____________________." Just then
G A B C' C

Dr. Piccolo's daughter came in the front door. "Aha!" cried Tones, pointing to the violin under her arm. "There is the thief!"

"Thief?" cried Dr. Piccolo's daughter. "I am no thief. Tomorrow is my father's birthday. I wanted to surprise him so I

(11.) ____________________ the violin without telling him
E D C F G

so I could take it in for **(12.)** ____________________.
F G A E D

"There you go, Professor," replied Tones. "The case is solved! Happy Birthday!" And with that, he walked out the front door.

Name ____

Musical Golf Tees

A miniature golf contest is being held at the Tee-Off Course. Help the players to find the musical *ti*s (7s) in the exercises below.

Write the name of each pitch using syllables or numbers.

1. 

___ ___ ___ ___

4. 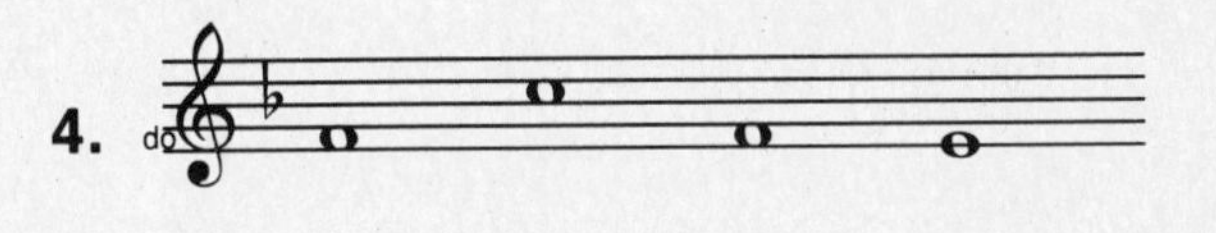

___ ___ ___ ___

2. 

___ ___ ___ ___

5. 

___ ___ ___ ___

3. 

___ ___ ___ ___

6. 

___ ___ ___ ___

Sing each exercise using syllables or numbers.

Write your own ending for each phrase below. Use *ti* (7) in each example.

Sing your compositions for a friend.

Name ______________________________

RESOURCE MASTER 1•8 Practice

Musical Symbol Review

On the left and right sides of the page are some of the musical signs that help guide musicians through a piece of music. At the bottom of the page are the meanings for the musical signs. See how much you remember by matching each musical sign with its meaning. Write the letter in the correct space. You may use some of the meanings more than once.

MUSICAL SIGNS

_____ **1.** $\frac{4}{4}$

_____ **2.** :‖

_____ **3.** 𝄻

_____ **4.** $\frac{2}{4}$

_____ **5.** 𝄞

_____ **6.** ♭

_____ **7.** ♯

_____ **8.** $\frac{6}{8}$

_____ **9.** 𝄾

_____ **10.** ⌈2. ⌉

MUSICAL SIGNS

_____ **11.** <

_____ **12.** 𝄽

_____ **13.** $\frac{3}{4}$

_____ **14.** |

_____ **15.** ‿

_____ **16.** ‖

_____ **17.** 𝅘𝅥 (x)

_____ **18.** ‖:

_____ **19.** 𝄼

_____ **20.** ⌈1. ⌉

MEANINGS

a. eighth rest
b. meter signature
c. first ending
d. treble clef
e. flat
f. whole rest
g. second ending
h. repeat sign
i. *crescendo*
j. bar line—end of measure
k. half rest
l. double bar—end of music
m. words are spoken, not sung
n. quarter rest
o. sharp
p. tie

Name ______________________________

Capriccio espagnol (excerpt)

by Nicolai Rimsky-Korsakov

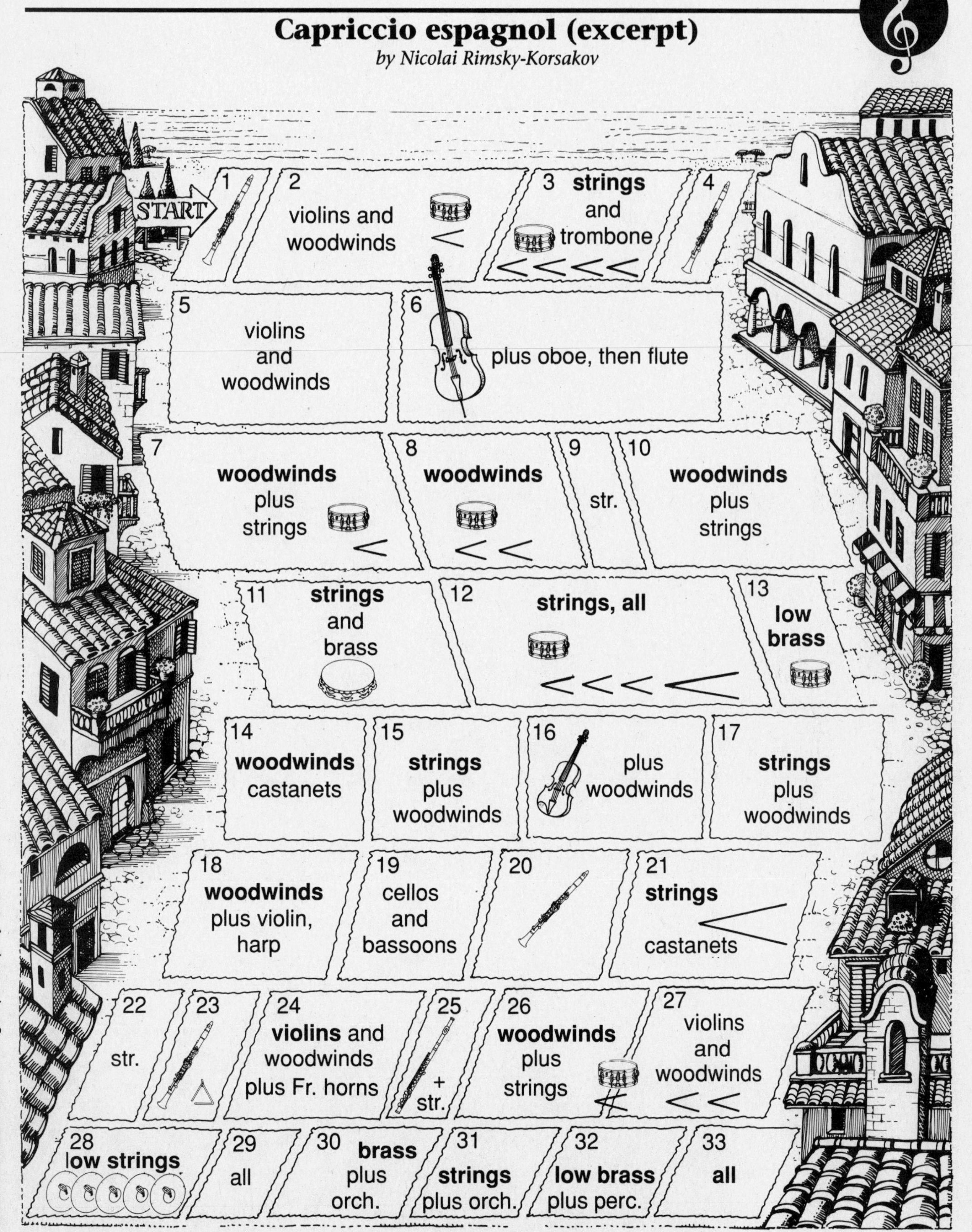

USING RESOURCE MASTER 1•9

DIRECTIONS:

Distribute a copy of the Resource Master to each student. Have students identify all the instruments on the Resource Master. You may wish to name an instrument and have students raise hands to tell you all locations of that instrument. (clarinet: boxes 1, 4, 20, 23; snare drum: boxes 2, 3, 7, 8, 12, 13, 26; cello: box 6; tambourine: box 11; violin: box 16; triangle: box 23; flute: box 25; cymbals: box 28)

Explain that instruments that are pictured on the listening map are featured or solo instruments. Single instruments named are the prominent accompanying instruments. Whole sections of the orchestra with the melody are also named, not pictured. Boldface instrument names indicate the most prominance. After listening ask students to tell which instrument families are featured prominently in this selection. (woodwind and string)

Name ______________________________

Check It Out

1. Which instruments do you hear?
   - a. brass and percussion
   - b. woodwinds and brass
   - c. strings
   - d. percussion

2. Which type of musical group do you hear?
   - a. band
   - b. orchestra
   - c. something else

3. Which rhythm pattern do you hear?

a. 

b. 

c. 

d.

4. Which example shows the pitches you hear?

a.

b. 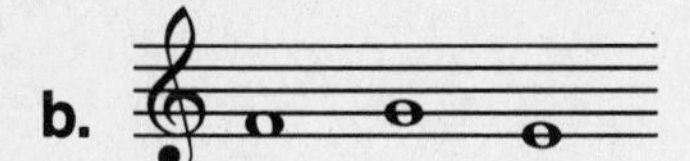

c.

d. 

Name ____________________

RESOURCE MASTER 2•1 Practice

Canon Instrumental Accompaniment

Henry Purcell

Name ____________________

Page 2

Part 1

Henry Purcell

Part 2

Henry Purcell

Part 3

Henry Purcell

Part 4

Henry Purcell

Name ______________________________

RESOURCE MASTER 2•1 Practice

Page 3

Name ______________________________

Canon Accompaniment for B♭ Instruments

Henry Purcell

Name ______________________________

RESOURCE MASTER 2•2 Practice

Page 2

Name ______________________________

RESOURCE MASTER 2•3 Practice

Playing the C Major Scale

Fill in the letter names of the pitches of the C major scale.

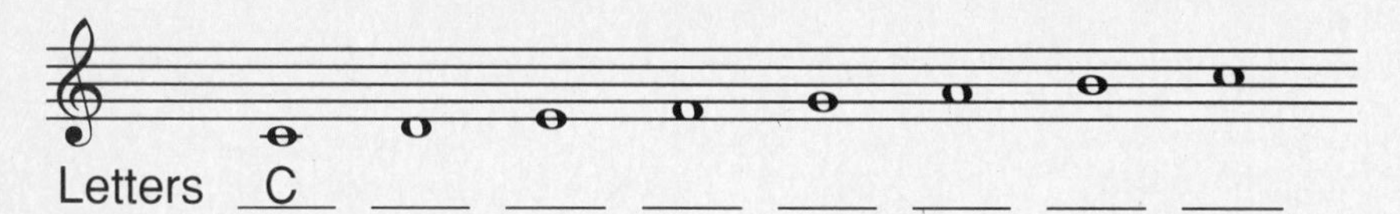

Letters C ___ ___ ___ ___ ___ ___ ___

Identify the pitches in this song. It uses the C major scale.
Write the letter names below each note.

Come Follow Me!

John Hilton

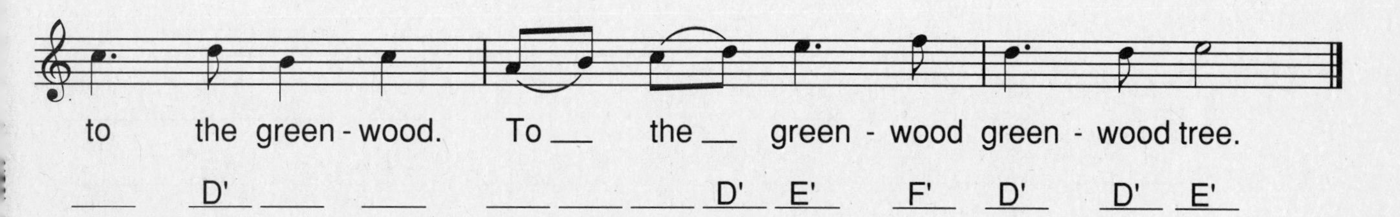

Play the song on the bells.

Name ______________________________

RESOURCE MASTER 2•4 Practice

Break the Code

You can send messages in musical "codes."

1. Decode this message by writing the letter name for each pitch on the line.

The detective saw the suspect's **a.** 

___ ___ ___ ___

in the crowd. "I **b.** 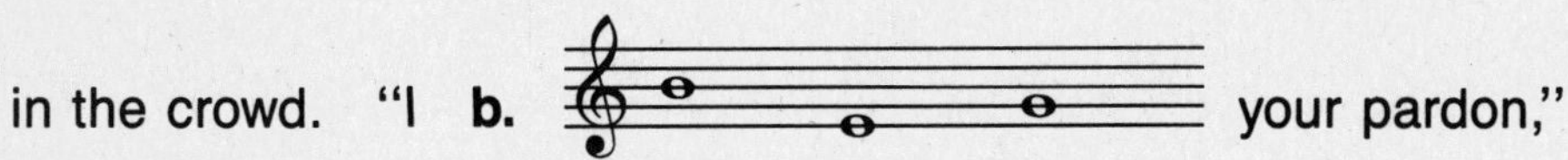 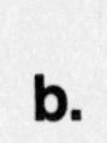 your pardon,"

___ ___ ___

she said, tapping his arm, "But can you come with me?"

"May I ask why?" he replied.

"You're wanted for questioning regarding the disappearance of

the man in the gorilla suit. You were seen standing next to

his **c.** "

___ ___ ___ ___

2. What other words can you write in musical code? Write at least ten words.

____________	____________
____________	____________
____________	____________
____________	____________
____________	____________
____________	____________

Name ______________________________

3. Write your own message. Use the musical code to write some of the words on a staff. Then give the message to a friend to decode!

____

____

____

____

____

____

Name ______________________________

RESOURCE MASTER 2•5 Assessment

Check It Out

1. Which rhythm do you hear?

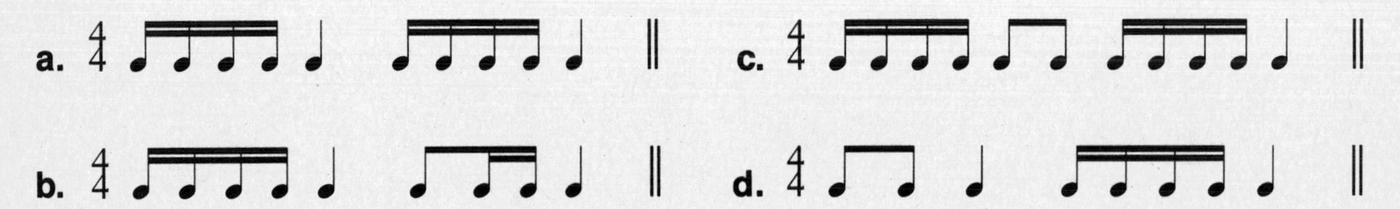

2. Which rhythm do you hear?

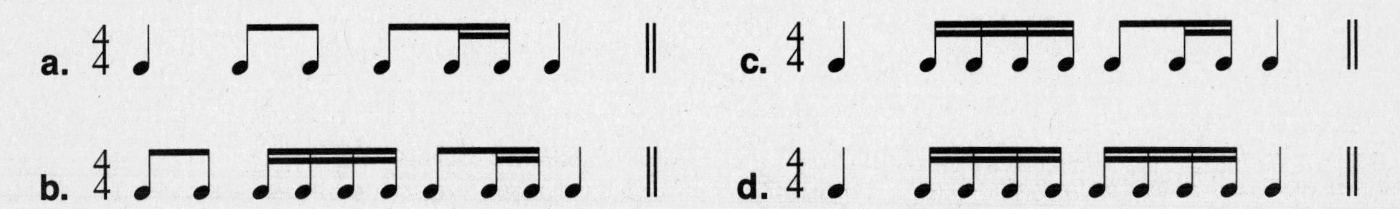

3. Do you hear a major scale?
a. Yes **b.** No

4. Do you hear a major scale?
a. Yes **b.** No

5. Do you hear A B A form?
a. Yes **b.** No

6. Do you hear A B A form?
a. Yes **b.** No

Name ____________________

Tempered Tuning

The strings of all keyboard instruments are tuned to particular pitches. Early methods of tuning required that the second pitch in a scale had a frequency that was 9/8 that of the first pitch. Frequency is the number of vibrations in a sound wave per second. The frequency of the third pitch was 10/8 that of the first pitch, and so on.

In these early methods, the same note had a different frequency (and pitch) in each scale. For example, the C in the C major scale had a different pitch from the C in the E♭ major scale. If you tried to play a song in the key of E♭ with your instrument tuned to the key of C, you sounded out of tune!

Eventually, someone worked out a method of tuning that worked for all scales, called *tempered tuning*. One solution, developed around 1700 and still used to tune pianos, was to multiply a pitch's frequency by 1.059 to get the frequency for the next pitch a half step higher.

Example:
Middle C has a frequency of 256 vibrations per second. C sharp is a half step above C, so its frequency is 256 x 1.059, or about 271.1. D is 271.1 x 1.059, or about 287.1.

J.S. Bach was so impressed with one type of tempered tuning that he wrote the 48 pieces of *The Well-Tempered Klavier* in the 24 possible keys—12 major and 12 minor. With tempered tuning, all could be played on the same instrument and still sound in tune.

Name ______________________________

RESOURCE MASTER 3•1

Page 2

Use a calculator. Find the frequencies of the pitches from C to C' to the nearest tenth using the tempered tuning method: Pitch × 1.059 = pitch of the note a half step higher.

Pitch	Frequency
C	256
C♯	271.1
D	287.1
E♭	______
E	______
F	______
F♯	______
G	______
G♯	______
A	______
B♭	______
B	______
C'	______

Name ________________________________

Playalong: "Hymn to Freedom"

Oscar Peterson
Arranged by Robert J. de Frece

Name ____________________

RESOURCE MASTER 3•2

Page 2

Name ______________________________

Page 3

Name ____________________

RESOURCE MASTER 3•2

Page 4

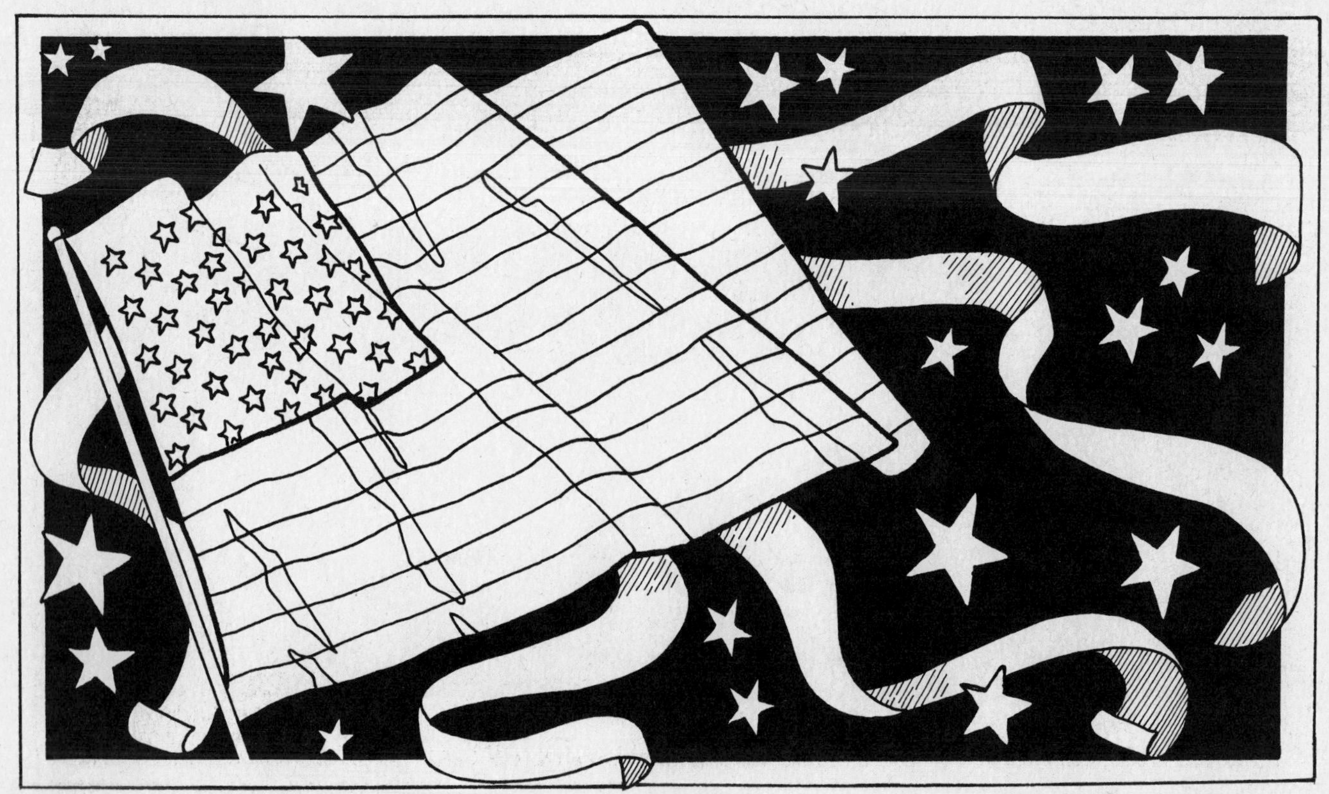

Name ____________________

Page 5

Name ______________________________

RESOURCE MASTER 3•2

Page 6

Hymn to Freedom

Name ____________________

Hymn to Freedom

Oscar Peterson
Arranged by Robert J. de Frece

Name ______________________________

RESOURCE MASTER 3•2

Page 8

Hymn to Freedom

Oscar Peterson
Arranged by Robert J. de Frece

Name ____________________

Hymn to Freedom

Name ______________________________

RESOURCE MASTER 3•2

Page 10

Name ____________________

Page 11

Hymn to Freedom

Name ____________________

RESOURCE MASTER 3•2

Page 12

Name ____________________

Dance the Mazurka!

The mazurka is a Polish melody and dance that was brought to Israel by Polish people. The following dance is a simple version of the original mazurka.

First practice the mazur step in place.

Beat 1 Step on right foot.
Beat 2 Step with the ball of the left foot behind the right heel.
Beat 3 Step with the right foot in place.
Beat 4 Step on left foot.
Beat 5 Step with the ball of the right foot behind the left heel.
Beat 6 Step with the left foot in place.

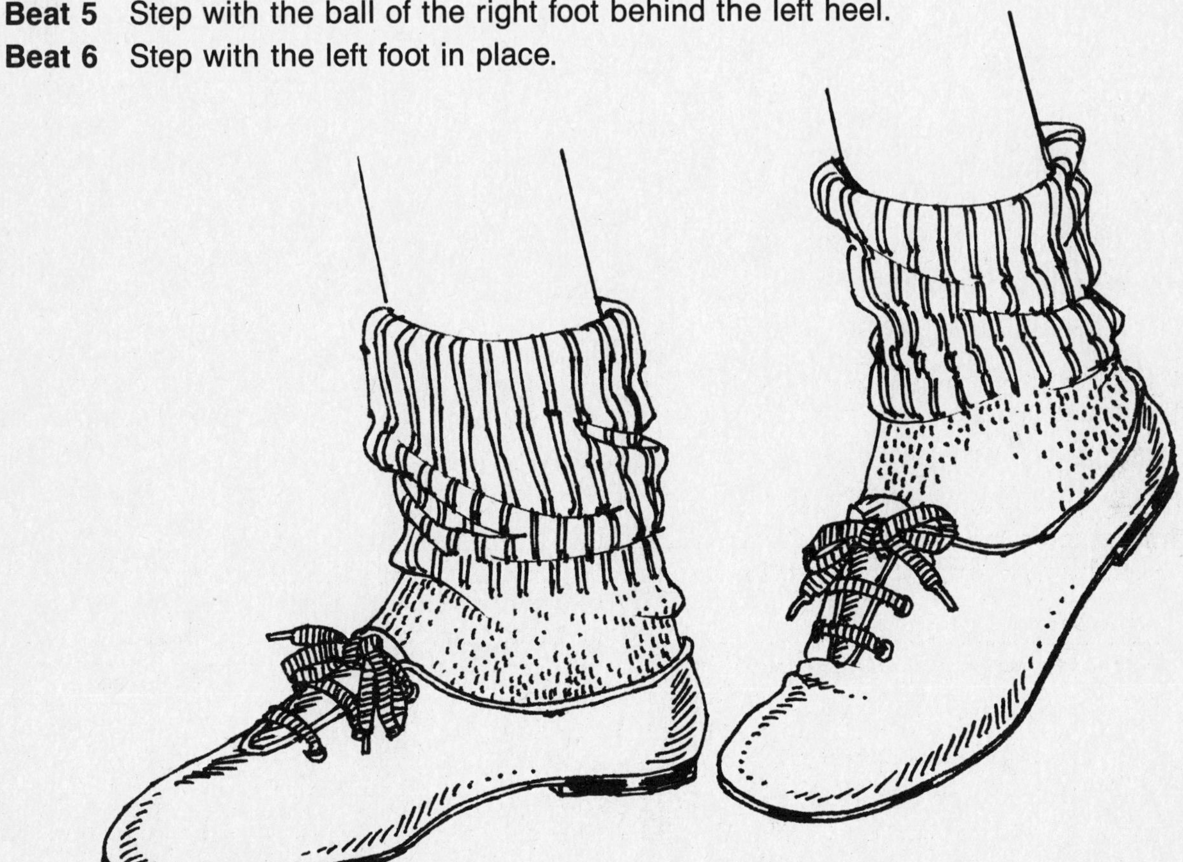

Name ______________________________

RESOURCE MASTER 3•3

Page 2

Now learn the mazurka.

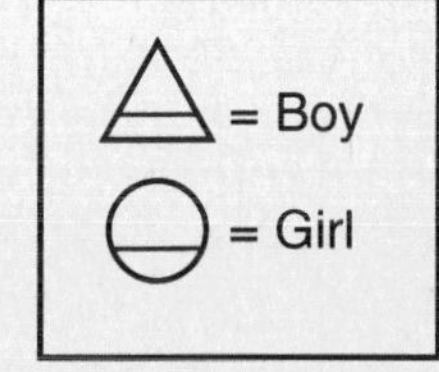

Formation: square of four couples facing clockwise

4 measure introduction:
partners stand in place

A section (Measures 1–16):
Each couple does 8 mazur steps forward, completing a trip around the square.

B section (Measures 17–32):
Boy spins girl clockwise with his right hand holding girl's right hand above her head, both continuing mazur step as they travel forward. On the 16th measure, they lower their right hands to waist level, keeping them joined and join left hands behind the right hands to prepare for the next step.

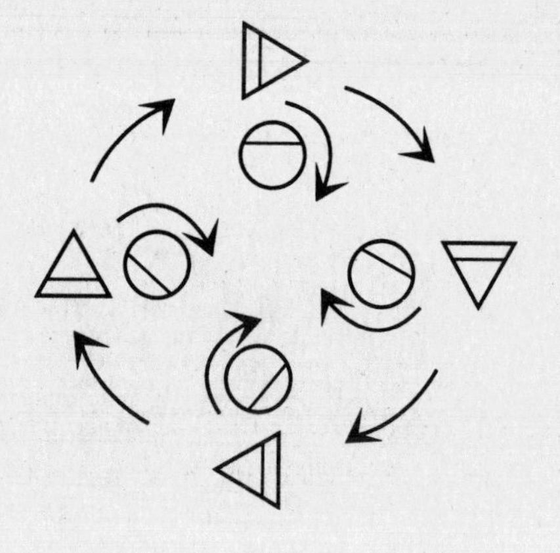

Hands:

C section (Measures 33–48):
Holubczyk (sweetheart step)—Partners hold left hands and right hands crossed in front as they stand side by side; boy does mazur step backwards and girl does the step forwards.

Hands:

Repeat these three sections two more times until the end of the recording.

Name ______________________________

Sonata in G Minor (The Cat's Fugue)

by Domenico Scarlatti (detailed)

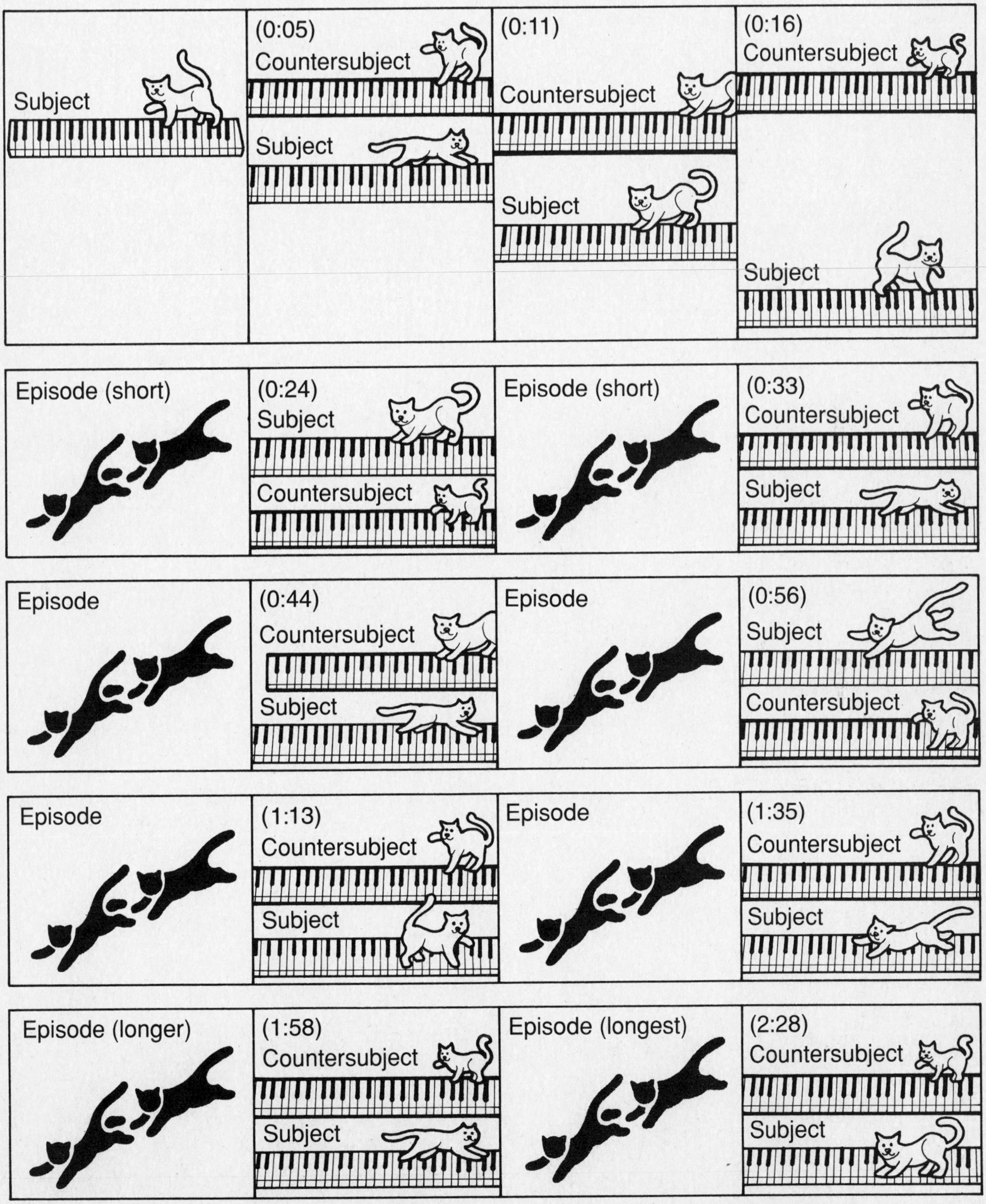

Subject	(0:05) Countersubject Subject	(0:11) Countersubject Subject	(0:16) Countersubject Subject
Episode (short)	(0:24) Subject Countersubject	Episode (short)	(0:33) Countersubject Subject
Episode	(0:44) Countersubject Subject	Episode	(0:56) Subject Countersubject
Episode	(1:13) Countersubject Subject	Episode	(1:35) Countersubject Subject
Episode (longer)	(1:58) Countersubject Subject	Episode (longest)	(2:28) Countersubject Subject

USING RESOURCE MASTER 3•4

DIRECTIONS:

Distribute a copy of the Resource Master to each student. Review the meaning of the terms *fugue, subject, countersubject,* and *episode.* Have students find all of the sections on the map with subject entries or subject and countersubject entries. Have them find the two places where the countersubject keyboard is placed below the subject keyboard. (second row, second box; third row last box)

Explain that the placement of each keyboard represents the relative pitch level at which it is heard. Have students find what is missing from the first row that is found in all other rows (episodes). You may wish to have students color all subject keyboards one color, countersubject keyboards another color, and episode boxes yet another color, to highlight contrast in the form.

Name ______________________________

Make and Tune a Thumb Piano

Materials

6″ x 6″ block of wood about 3/4 inch thick
smallstick
1/4″ dowel (optional)
screwdriver
8–10 popsicle sticks
2 screws
drill (optional)

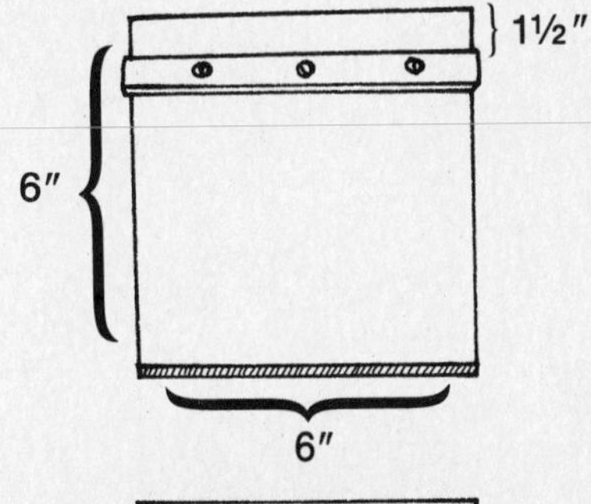

Step 1 Use three screws to attach the small stick loosely to the 6″ x 6″ block of wood about 1½ inch down.

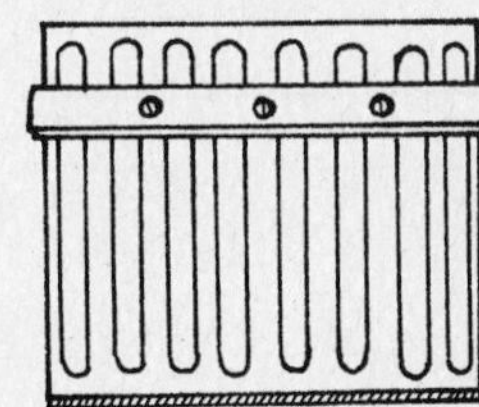

Step 2 Place eight popsicle sticks in parallel lines under one end of the small stick.

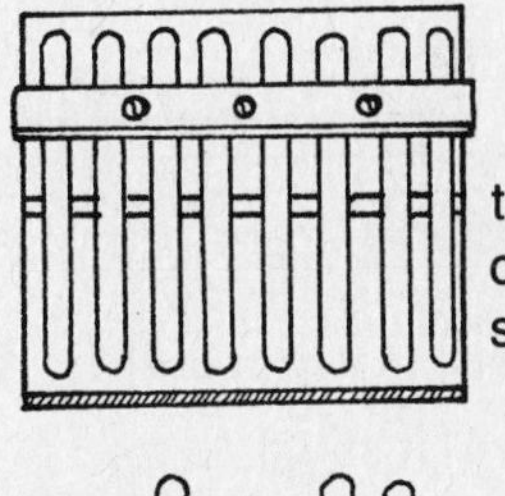

thin stick (a ¼″ dowel or two stacked popsicle sticks)

Step 3 Tighten the screws so that the small stick almost touches the popsicle sticks. Push a thin stick under the popsicle sticks as far toward the cross stick as it will go.

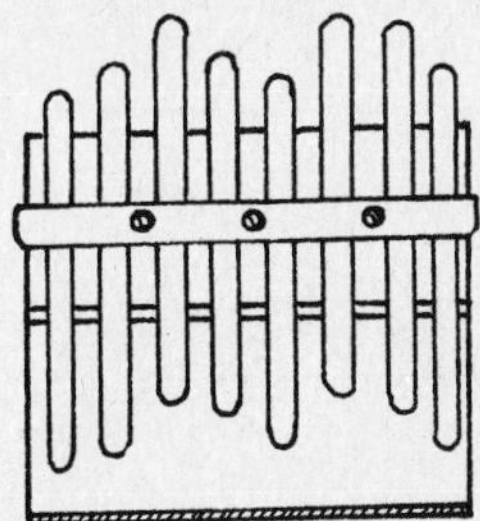

Step 4 Play the thumb piano by striking the prongs with the thumbs. Tune it by sliding the popsicle sticks forward or backward. Experiment with the position of the sticks.

What did you discover about the relationship between the length of the vibrating part (popsicle stick) and the pitch? ______________________________

____

Name ______________________________

RESOURCE MASTER 3•6 Practice

Group Melody

Work with a group to create a short melody
—eight measures of $\frac{2}{4}$.

The melody should begin and end on C
and use at least one ♪. ♬ combination.

Use any of these pitches: A$_{\vert}$ C D E G A.

Each pitch must equal one beat, for example,
♩, ♫, or ♪. ♬

Notate your melody below.

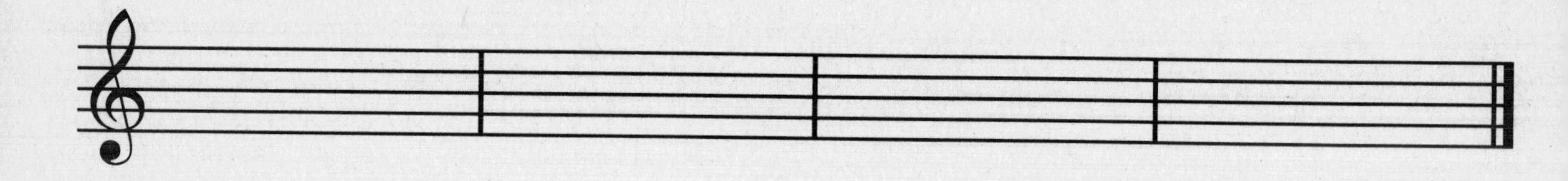

Name ____

Check It Out

1. Which rhythm do you hear?

a. $\frac{4}{4}$

c. $\frac{4}{4}$

b. $\frac{4}{4}$

d. $\frac{4}{4}$

2. Which rhythm do you hear?

a. $\frac{3}{4}$

c. $\frac{3}{4}$

b. $\frac{3}{4}$

d. $\frac{3}{4}$

3. Which keyboard instrument do you hear?
   a. piano **b.** pipe organ **c.** harpsichord

4. How is this keyboard sound produced?

   a. A hammer hits a string.
   b. Air vibrates in a tube.
   c. A string is plucked.

Name ____________________

RESOURCE MASTER 4•1 Practice

"Away to America" Rhythmic Building Blocks

Cut out the rhythmic building blocks. Arrange them to create your own accompaniment to "Away to America."

Name ______________________________

"El tambor" Rhythmic Building Blocks

Cut out the rhythmic building blocks. Arrange them to create your own accompaniment to "El tambor."

Name ____________________

RESOURCE MASTER 4•3 Practice

"Üsküdar" Rhythms

Cut out these measures of $\frac{2}{4}$. Put them in correct order to match the rhythm of the words in "Üsküdar."

Name ________________________________

Ukulele Chords for "Hoe Ana"

Learn these chords on the ukulele. Then play them with "Hoe Ana." Strum on the dotted-quarter-note beat.

Ukulele Chords for D Tuning

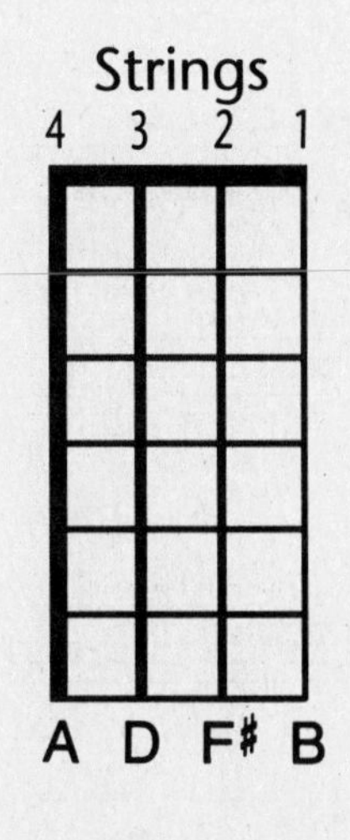

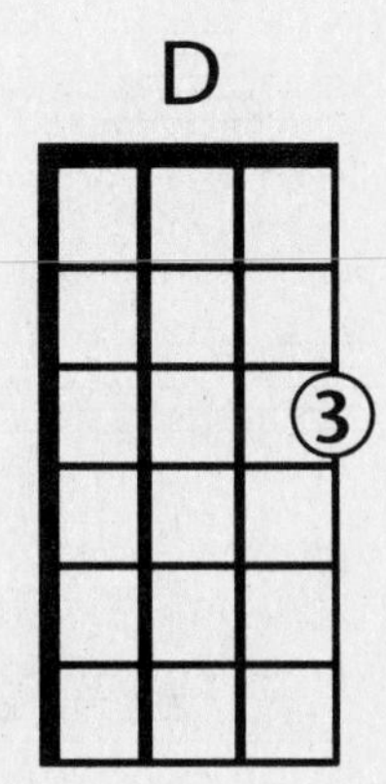

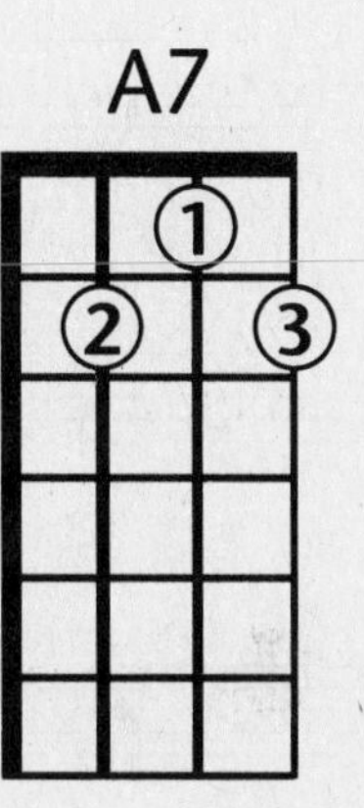

Strums or strokes: Using the first finger of the right hand, brush/strum downward over the strings with the back of the nail for the down stroke. For the up stroke, bring the flesh of the fingertip back up.

Name ______________________________

RESOURCE MASTER 4•5 Practice

"Movin' On" Accompaniment

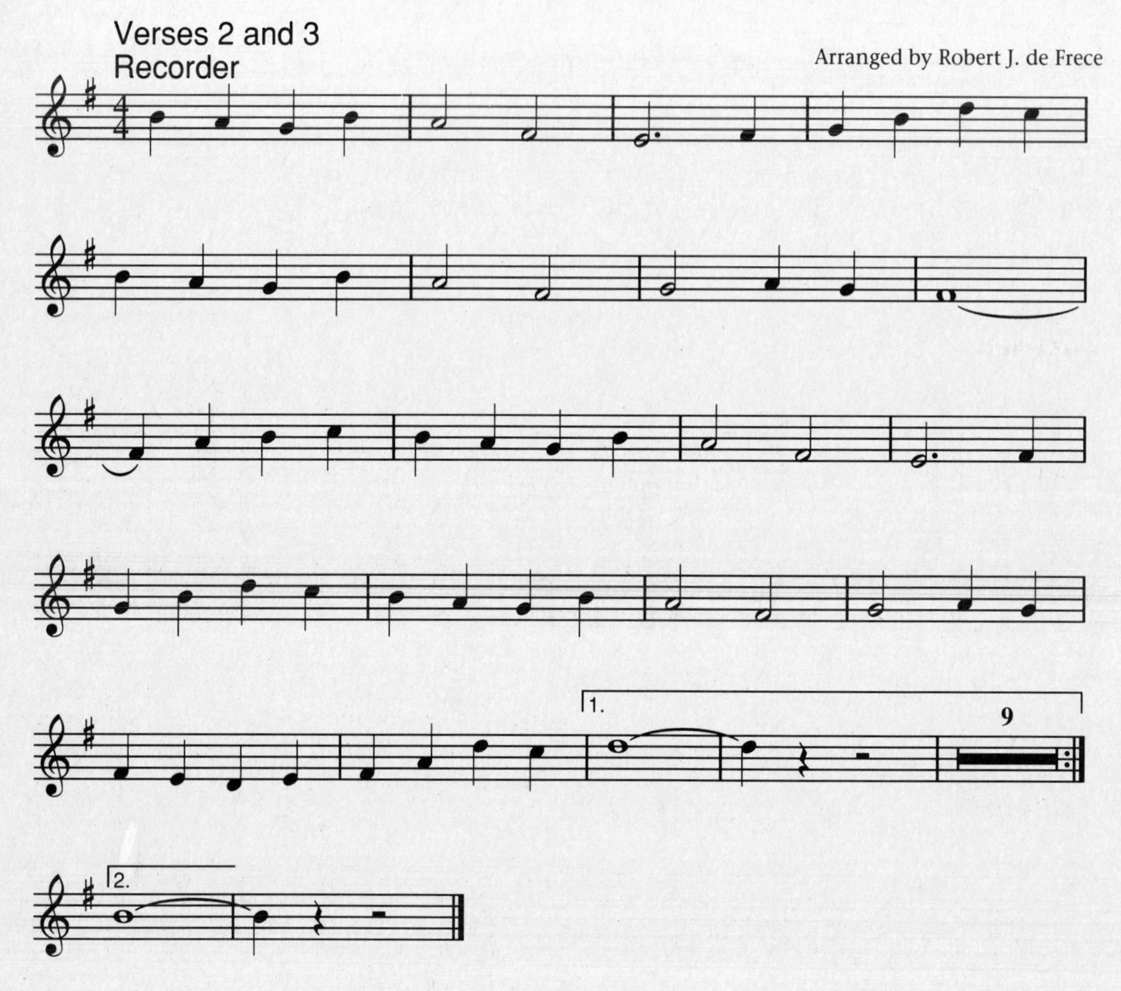

Name ____

Bells Required (22)

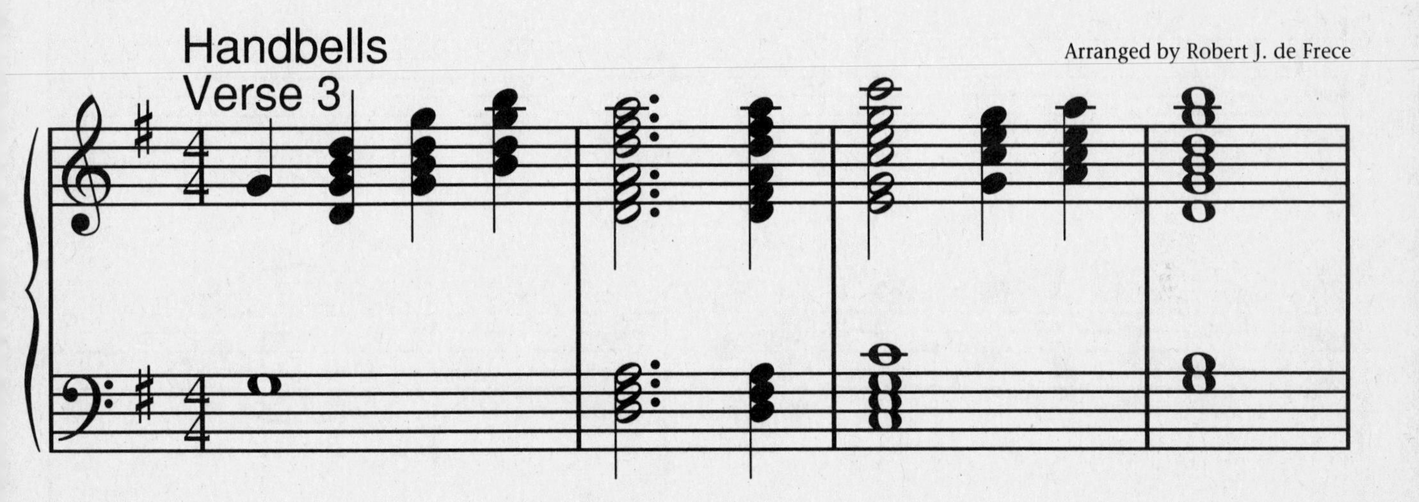
Handbells
Verse 3
Arranged by Robert J. de Frece

Name ____________________

RESOURCE MASTER 4•5

Page 3

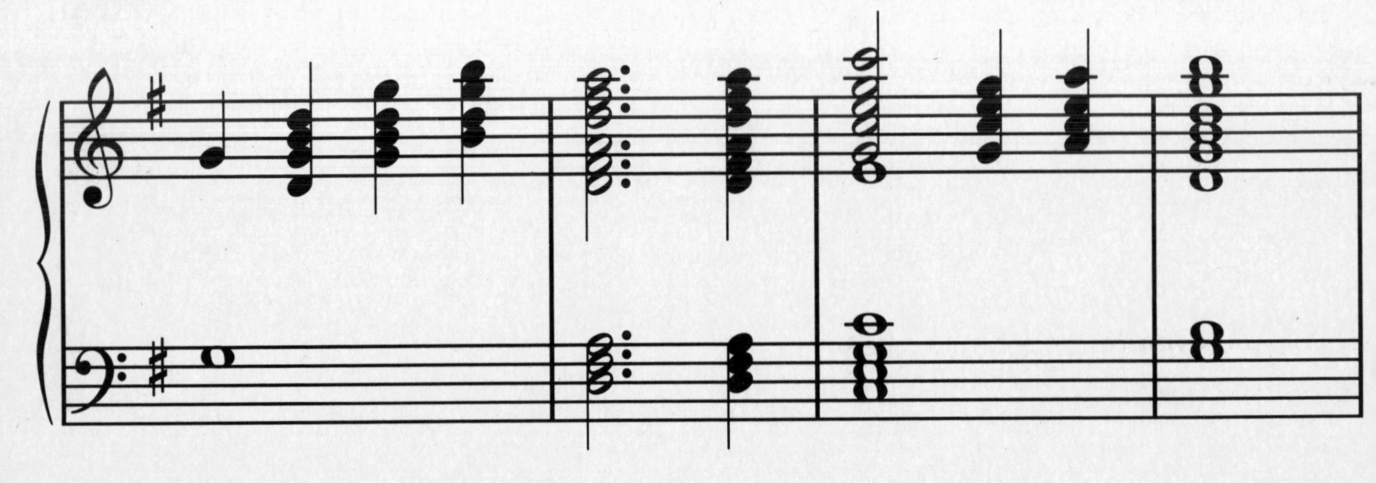

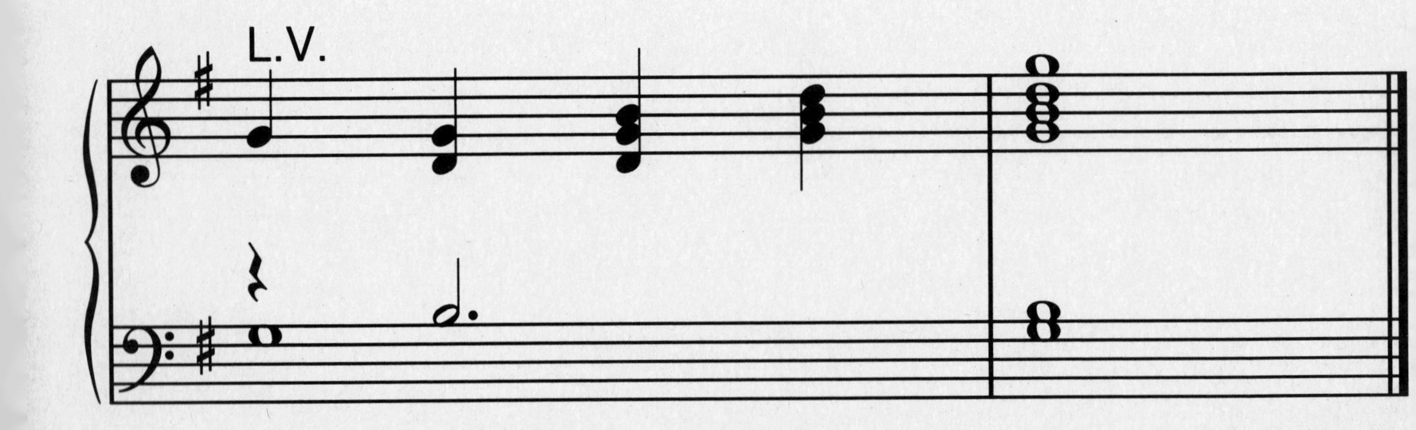

Name ____

RESOURCE MASTER 4•6 Assessment

Check It Out

1. Do you hear the first five steps of a minor scale?

a. Yes **b.** No

2. Do you hear the first five steps of a minor scale?

a. Yes **b.** No

3. Which rhythm do you hear?

a. 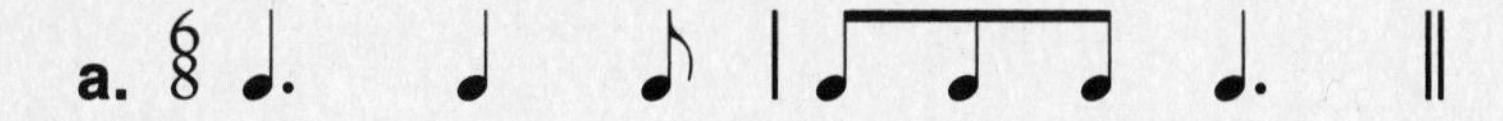

b. 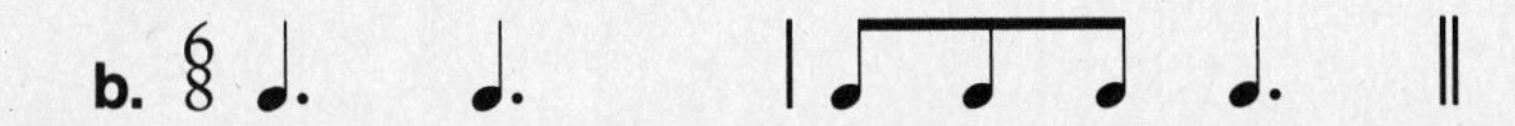

c. 

d. 

4. Which rhythm do you hear?

a.

b. 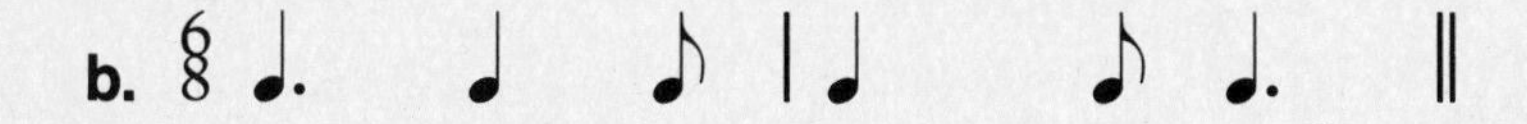

c.

d.

Name ____________________

RESOURCE MASTER 4•7 Practice

Dance to "Red River Valley"

Promenade

Swing

Grand Chain

The square dance is the only style of folk dance that is directed by a caller. He or she will either call a standard version of the dance or combine square dance moves to improvise a new version.

Practice these common square dance calls:

Promenade: Walk in pairs, holding hands, in a counterclockwise direction using a smooth, gliding walk.

Sometimes the hands are held in a "skating" position: girl's right hand holding boy's right hand; girl's left hand holding boy's left hand. Try the promenade with the hands held in the skating position.

Swing: Partners stand right sides together, girl's right hand in boy's left hand at shoulder height and boy's right hand on the left side of girl's waist. Turn clockwise.

Grand chain: Girls face clockwise, boys face counterclockwise.

Couples join right hands (as if shaking hands) and pull by right shoulder to right shoulder.

Join left hands with the next person met and pull by left shoulder to left shoulder. Release hands and continue as directed.

Name ______________________________

Square Dance for "Red River Valley"

Formation: Four couples in a square, all facing the inside of the square. The boy is always on the girl's left.

Couple 1
girl boy

Couple 2 boy girl

Couple 4 girl boy

Couple 3
boy girl

FIGURE

Caller says: First couple lead down the valley.	*Dancers:* Couple 1 walks counterclockwise to face Couple 2.
You circle to the left and to the right.	Couple 1 join hands and circle with Couple 2.
Then you swing with the girl in the valley, and you swing with that Red River gal.	Couple 1 swings with Couple 2, then each person swings with own partner.
Then you lead right on down the valley. . . (Repeat all steps with Couples 3 and 4.)	Couple 1 travels to Couple 3, repeats the above, then travels to Couple 4.
Caller says: Do an Allemande left on your corner.	*Dancers:* Join left hands with the person to the corner and swing around once.
And a grand right and left half way around.	All couples do a grand chain, until each person meets own partner.
Then promenade home with your darling. Promenade with that Red River gal.	Walk around the circle with partner until you reach home (starting position).

Name ____________________

RESOURCE MASTER 5•1 Practice

Voice Categories

The four major adult, or changed voice, categories are soprano, alto, tenor, and bass.

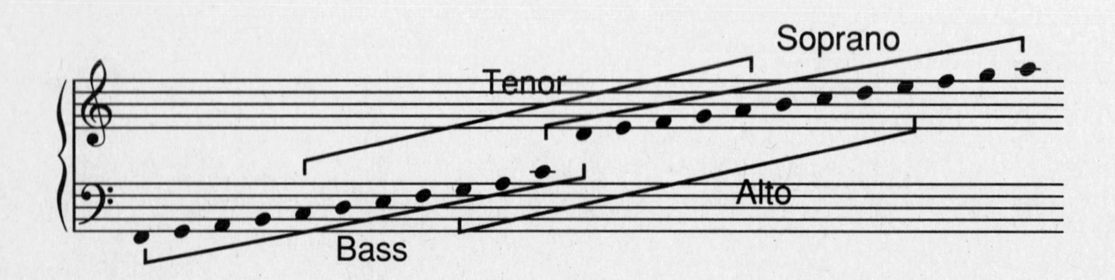

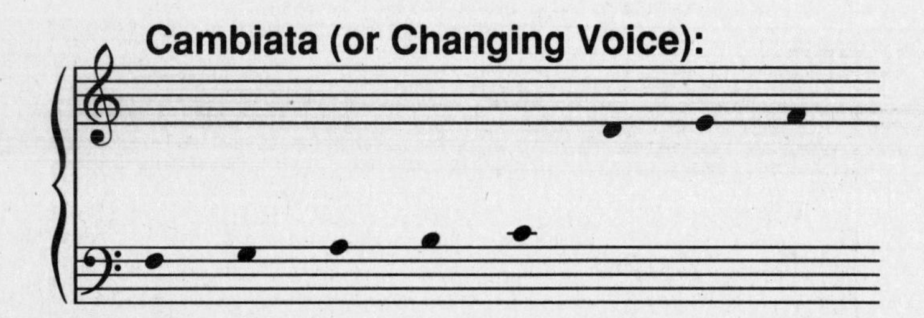

Play (or listen to) the pitches belonging to each voice category.

1. Which voice category is the highest? the lowest? ____________________

____

2. Which adult voice category is closest to the cambiata category? ____________________
3. Try singing the pitches in each category. Which category

   does your voice fit into? ____________________

Name ______________________________

Lighter and Heavier Vocal Tone Color

Tone color refers to the different qualities of sound. Imagine two instruments playing exactly the same pitch, one after another. Think about how you can tell which instrument you are hearing. You can tell them apart because each has a distinctive tone color.

Each singer also has a distinctive tone color. A singer can also produce several different tone colors. Two of these are sometimes called light and heavy tone color.

Most of the time, singers with unchanged voices use a lighter voice quality. However, in some songs the heavier voice is more appropriate to the style. With awareness of how it works, the heavier tone color can be used without hurting the voice. However, care must always be taken not to strain the voice, when using the heavier tone color, by singing too loudly or using it for too long a period of time.

Any tone color should always be used with good posture and breathing and with open, free vowels sung without straining or forcing.

Folk singers from many cultures around the world often use the heavier mechanism. It is also often heard in show tunes and popular songs. You need to consider not one, but a variety of ways of singing, and you need to hear different tone colors in vocal production and vocal styles in order to hear and imitate different styles.

Name ____________________

RESOURCE MASTER 5•3 Practice

Predictions, Predictions!

Interpretation involves using musical elements in an appropriate way. Look at the words and illustrations for "Won't You Charleston with Me?" Think about how you might interpret this song.

Then make predictions about the vocal interpretation you will be hearing on the recording by circling the words in the *Prediction* columns that you think will best describe the musical elements that you will hear. Be prepared to back up your ideas with good reasons.

MUSICAL ELEMENTS	PREDICTION	
tempo	fast	slow
dynamics	loud	soft
tone color	light	heavy
articulation	legato	marcato

Name ______________________________

The Critic Reviews

Pretend you are a critic writing a review of the music you just heard. Fill in the blanks.

Title of Review ______________________________

By ______________________________
Music Times Critic

In this reviewer's opinion, ______________ should be performed
(song title)

with ______________ articulation, ______________________________ dynamics,
legato/marcato *soft/medium soft/medium loud/loud*

______________________________ tempo and ______________________________
slow/medium slow/medium fast/fast *bright/light/floating/heavy/rough*

tone color.

The performance I heard today was so ____________________ that I rushed
wonderful/questionable
to my computer to get my words into print at once.

To my __________________, I heard ______________ articulation.
surprise/satisfaction *legato/marcato*

The music still rings in my ears, partly because the dynamics were

so ______________________________ .
soft/medium soft/medium loud/loud

The tempo ______________ the one I would have chosen. It was
was/was not

______________________________.
slow/medium slow/medium fast/fast

The ______________________________ tone color was ____________________.
bright/light/floating/dark/heavy *delightful/outrageous*

I ______________________________ that you see the next performance!
recommend/do not recommend

Name ____________________

RESOURCE MASTER 5•5 Background

Gianni Schicchi Summary

CAST OF CHARACTERS

Gianni Schicchi—A new citizen of Florence
Lauretta—His daughter
The Donati Family:
Buoso—A wealthy man (deceased)
Rinuccio—A nephew of Buoso's who is in love with Lauretta
Zita—Buoso's cousin and Rinuccio's aunt
Simone—Buoso's (male) cousin
Gherardo—Buoso's nephew
Nella—Gherardo's wife
Gherardino—Gherardo and Nella's son
Marco—Buoso's nephew
Ciesca—Marco's wife
Betto—Buoso's brother-in-law

Witnesses (2)
Doctor
Lawyer

SETTING

Florence, 1299 A.D. (Florence is now a city in Italy.)

SUMMARY OF MUSICAL SELECTIONS AND PLOT:

Listen to the Opening Scene.
(See page 213.) This sets the comic tone of the opera. Zita, Simone, Rinuccio, Ciesca, Marco, Gherardo, Nella, and Betto are around the bed, weeping over the wealthy Buoso, who has just died.

It soon becomes apparent that they are more concerned for their inheritance than for Buoso's death. Each relative tries to seem more upset than the others.
The first says, "I'll weep for days and days."
The next says, "For days? For months!"
The next, "Months? For years and years!"
Finally, one says, ". . . for all my life!"

As they talk, Gherardo's young son is playing in the room and the adults occasionally shoo him away. The scene ends as Zita crossly says, "Portatecelo voi, Gherardo, via!" ("Take the child away, Gherardo.")

Continuation of the Plot:

ALL: Oh, Buoso, Buoso, we'll spend the rest of our lives crying over our loss! *(They all cry and weep loudly. Then, Nella and Betto whisper in each other's ears.)*
ZITA: What are you whispering about?
BETTO: Well—I heard at the bakery that Buoso left everything to the monastery.
ALL: What? Oh, no! What will we do?
SIMONE: Wait—maybe it's not true! But, on the other hand, maybe we'd better find that will quickly, before any one else does. It's our only hope!
(They frantically search the room, looking for the will.)
RINUCCIO: Aunt, I found it! As a reward, maybe you'll finally let me marry Lauretta.
ZITA: If we inherit the money we deserve, you can marry anyone you like—dowry or not!
RINUCCIO: *(To the little boy, Gherardino)* Go and fetch Gianni Schicchi and tell him to come here and bring Lauretta at once!
(Gherardino runs off. Zita tears open the will. She tries to read it as the others look at it over her shoulder. Their faces register more and more horror as they read.)
SIMONE: It's true! It's actually true! He really has left it all to the monastery! *(They all* really *begin to cry.)*
RINUCCIO: There's only one person who can save us!
ALL: Who?
RINUCCIO: Gianni Schicchi!
ZITA: I don't want to hear another word about him or his daughter. He's just a peasant from the country.

Listen to "Firenze è come un albero fiorito (Florence is like a blossoming tree)."

(See page 214 and follow the description of the story as you listen.)
Rinuccio claims that newcomers to Florence like Gianni Schicchi will make the city richer and more splendid, just as soil and water nourish a tree.

Name ____________________

Page 3

Continuation of the Plot:

(Gianni Schicchi enters.)

GIANNI: How upset they look! Buoso must have gotten better! *(Lauretta and Rinuccio greet each other warmly. Gianni is told that the relatives have been disinherited.)*

ZITA: I'll not give my nephew to a girl without a dowry!

GIANNI: Bravo, Zita, Bravo! For the sake of a dowry, you ruin their lives! You stingy miser, you!

RINUCCIO: You *will* help us won't you, Gianni Schicchi?

GIANNI: Never! Help people like these? No! Never! *(Lauretta moves to him. The others sit down.)*

Listen to "O mio babbino caro (Oh, my dear Daddy)."

(See page 215 and follow the description of the aria as you listen.)

Lauretta begs her father to help with the relatives' plot so that she can have a dowry (money or property given to the husband's family at a wedding). Her last line is "Babbo, pietà, pietà . . ." ("Daddy, have pity, have pity!")

Continuation of the Plot:

GIANNI: Oh, give me the will! *(Looks at it. They all lean forward.)* Nothing can be done. . . *(All slump in their chairs.)*. . . and yet!. . . *(They jump to their feet and surround him. He speaks to the relatives.)* No one knows that Buoso has taken his last breath? *(They shake their heads.)* Good! Take Buoso into the next room. Hurry! *(Two of the men carry Buoso off. There is a knock on the door.)* Oh! Who can that be?

ZITA: It's the doctor!

GIANNI: Don't let him all the way in! Tell him Buoso's resting. *(He quickly puts on Buoso's nightcap, climbs under the bedcovers, with only his nose showing.)*

(The relatives open the door partway and block it to keep the doctor from entering.)

DOCTOR: May I come in?

THE RELATIVES: *(Sweetly, but firmly holding the door only partway open.)* Good day, doctor! Buoso's much better! He's resting comfortably! We won't need you today!

Name ____________________

Page 4

DOCTOR: I really should see him!
GIANNI: *(Sleepily, imitating Buoso)* No, doctor, I am much improved, but I need to rest! Please come again this evening.
DOCTOR: I can tell he's better by his voice! *(To himself)* What a great doctor I must be! *(To the others)* Till tonight, then!
THE RELATIVES and GIANNI: Till tonight! *(They close the door in his face.)*
GIANNI: *(Sitting up)* Now, Rinuccio, go get the lawyer at once. Tell him that Buoso wants to make a new will. And tell him to bring two witnesses. *(Rinuccio runs out.)*
THE RELATIVES: *(Crowding around Gianni Schicchi)* Oh, Schicchi! How wonderful! How clever you are! Now, we will all share in the fortune that is rightfully ours. We can each have one of the farms or estates and divide the cash equally among us.
ZITA: But wait! That still leaves the mule, this house, and the mills at Signa. *I* want *them*!
MARCO: They're the best items. We *all* want them!
GIANNI: So much for family love.
SIMONE: I say that we should all rely on Schicchi's sense of honor and decency to decide who gets what.
RELATIVES: Oh, very well. *(With artificial sincerity)* Of course, we trust Schicchi—and each other!
ZITA: *(Giving him the nightcap as she whispers to him)* If you leave me the mule, the house and the mills, I'll give you thirty florins. *(Gianni smiles. The two shake hands.)*
SIMONE: *(Whispering to him)* If you leave me the mule, the house and the mills, I'll give you a hundred florins. *(Gianni smiles. They shake hands.)*
BETTO: *(Whispering to him)* If you leave me the mule, the house and the mills, I'll stuff your pockets full of money. *(Gianni smiles. They shake hands.)*
NELLA: *(Whispering to him as she gives him a handkerchief)* If you leave me the mule, the house and the mills, I'll smother you in florins. *(Gianni smiles. They shake hands.)*
CIESCA: *(Giving him the nightshirt, whispering to him.)* If you leave me the mule, the house and the mills, a thousand florins to you. *(Gianni smiles. They shake hands.)*

Name ____

RESOURCE MASTER 5•5 Background

Page 5

GIANNI: Now, I must warn you that the law will punish us all severely if we are ever found out. Do you understand?
THE RELATIVES: We understand!
(A knock is heard. Gianni jumps into bed. Rinuccio enters with the lawyer and the two witnesses.)
GIANNI: Gentlemen! Thank you for coming! *(He extends a trembling hand.)* I am shaking from my illness, so you will have to write the will for me as I dictate it.
LAWYER: Oh, you poor man! Of course. See, I have brought the witnesses.
GIANNI: Good! Let us begin. The first part of the will remains the same. Each relative receives one farm or estate. The cash money I leave in equal portions to each.
THE RELATIVES: Oh, thank you! Thank you! Now we come to the mule, the house, and the mills.
GIANNI: I leave the best mule in the country to. . . my devoted friend, Gianni Schicchi!
RELATIVES: What? What's that? What can he want with the mule?
GIANNI: I know what Gianni Schicchi wants. I leave my house in Florence to. . . my dear friend, Gianni Schicchi.
RELATIVES: Oh, that's enough, enough! We protest!
GIANNI: *(Pretending to be dying)* Goodbye, Florence. . .
LAWYER: Don't go against the wishes of the dying man!
GIANNI: I leave the mills to. . . my close friend, Gianni Schicchi!
LAWYER: Thank you. *(He leaves with the witnesses.)*

Listen to "Ladro! Ladro! (Thief! Thief!)"

(See page 215 and follow along as you listen.)
The furious relatives scream, "Thief! Thief!" at Gianni Schicchi for tricking them and keeping Buoso's best property for himself. They try to steal things from the house, which now belongs to Schicchi. Schicchi chases them away, yelling, "Get out! Go!" Now that Gianni Schicchi is rich, his daughter will have her dowry. Lauretta and Rinuccio are happy that they will be able to be married.

THE END

Name ____________________

Style Chart for *Gianni Schicchi* Arias

Circle the words that best describe these musical elements in each aria.

Aria	Tempo	Dynamics	Tone Color	Articulation	Voice Category
Rinuccio "Firenze è come un albero fiorito"	slow medium fast fast very fast	very soft (***pp***) soft (***p***) medium soft (***mp***) medium loud (***mf***) loud (***f***)	light bright floating heavy dark hushed	smooth and connected (legato) strongly accented (marcato)	soprano alto tenor bass
Lauretta "O mio babbino caro"	slow medium fast fast very fast	very soft (***pp***) soft (***p***) medium soft (***mp***) medium loud (***mf***) loud (***f***)	light bright floating heavy dark hushed	smooth and connected (legato) strongly accented (marcato)	soprano alto tenor bass

Name ____________________

RESOURCE MASTER 5•7 Practice

The Composer's Workshop

You can compose by using tools from the composer's toolbox: tempo, instrumentation, dynamics, melody, harmony, and rhythm.

Here's the poem you will set to music:

> There's music in a hammer. . .
> There's music in a nail. . .
> There's music in a little cat
> If you step upon its tail.
> —Anonymous

Starting Your Composition

There are many different ways of starting an original music work. You can begin with any of the composer's tools above, or even with two others. The other two are form and texture.

For now try working with the tools in the order in which they are shown. The important thing is to try to think like a composer. This will help you understand more about what a composer does to create original music sounds. Then, when you listen to music in the future, perhaps you will think about all the choices a composer makes.

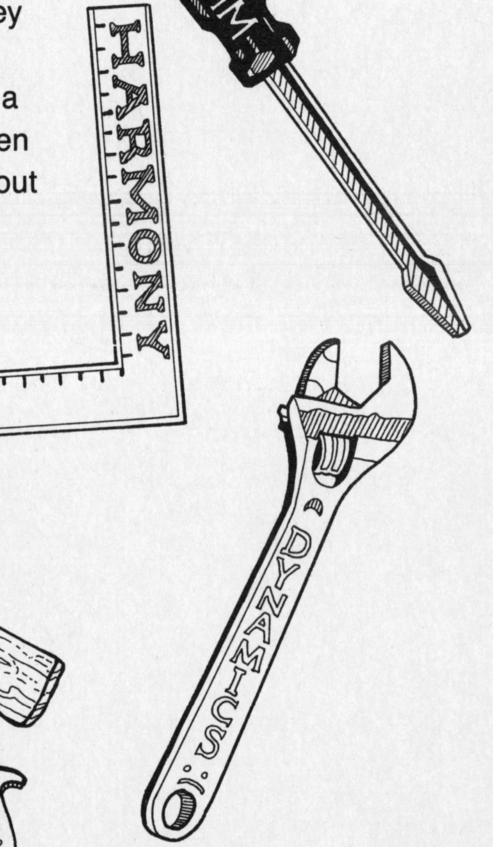

Name ____________________

Step 1: Select your tempo.
Tempo is the speed of the beat. There are many, many choices for tempo. A few are listed below.

Choose one of the following tempos:

slow (*adagio*)	moderate (*moderato*)
fast (*allegro*)	very fast (*presto*)

Write the tempo you select on the line.

TEMPO

____

Step 2: Select your instrumentation for the accompaniment patterns.
You will need two different sounds for the accompaniment patterns. Just for fun, since the poem mentions tools, try to use at least two carpenter's tools along with traditional instruments. You can use saws, hammer, ratchets, nails, bolts, measuring tape, T-squares, or wrenches. You may want to use some other sound sources as well. It's up to you! You will figure out how you are going to use them later, so don't worry too much about that right now.

List the instruments and tools you select for the accompaniment patterns below. You can use fewer instruments than the number of lines shown here, but try to use at least two.

INSTRUMENTATION

____

____

____

____

Name ________________

RESOURCE MASTER 5•7 Practice

Page 3

Step 3: Decide on dynamics.

You will want to select dynamics that seem appropriate. From softest to loudest, four of the possibilities are:

very soft (*pianissimo*) soft (*piano*)
loud (*forte*) very loud (*fortissimo*)

You may want to use more than one of these. Read the poem again and decide how loud it will be at the beginning and at the end. You may also want to change dynamics within the poem and plan dynamics for your instruments. Feel free! After all, you're the composer! Write your decisions below.

Beginning dynamic level: ________________

There's music in a hammer,

There's music in a nail,

There's music in a little cat

If you step upon its tail!

Ending dynamic level: ________________

Ideas for dynamics for the instrumental accompaniment

patterns: ________________

____

____

____

____

Name ____

Step 4: Create your melody.

There are twelve pitches in the composer's toolbox. For today, try working with just five of them—the ones marked below with arrows.

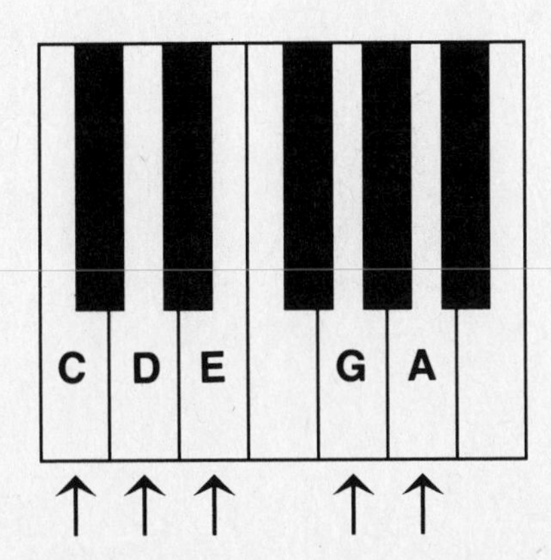

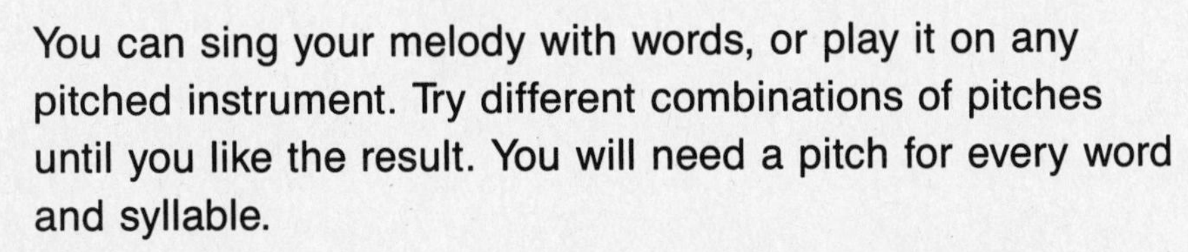

You can sing your melody with words, or play it on any pitched instrument. Try different combinations of pitches until you like the result. You will need a pitch for every word and syllable.

Record your melody by writing the letter names of the pitches you chose on the blank line over each word or syllable.

____	____	____	____	____	____	____	
There's	mu -	sic	in	a	ham -	mer,	
____	____	____	____	____	____		
There's	mu -	sic	in	a	nail,		
____	____	____	____	____	____	____	____
There's	mu -	sic	in	a	lit -	tle	cat
____	____	____	____	____	____	____	
If	you	step	up -	on	its	tail!	

Name ________________________________

RESOURCE MASTER 5•7 Practice

Page 5

Step 5: Add harmony.
Chords are used to accompany a melody. Chords are combinations of three or more pitches. There are many chords that a composer can use, but for now try using just the two chords below.

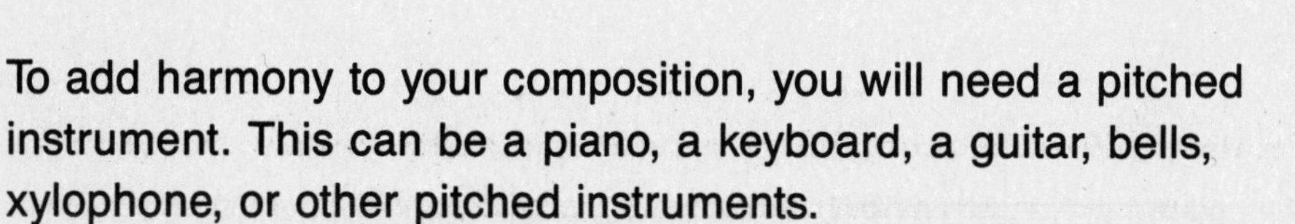

To add harmony to your composition, you will need a pitched instrument. This can be a piano, a keyboard, a guitar, bells, xylophone, or other pitched instruments.

Decide where you will play each chord. Write the pitch letter names of one of the chords on the line under each underlined word or syllable.

There's *mu* - sic in a *ham* - mer,

_______ _______

There's *mu* - sic in a *nail*,

_______ _______

There's *mu* - sic in a *lit* - tle cat

_______ _______

If you *step* upon its *tail*!

_______ _______

Name ____

Step 6: Select the rhythm for the accompaniment.
Below are some of the rhythms you might choose to have played as accompaniment patterns on the instruments or other sound sources you selected. You can use these rhythms or make up your own.

Pattern 1: 2/4 ♩ ♩ | ♩ 𝄽 ‖

Pattern 2: 2/4 ♪ ♩ ♪ | ♩ 𝄽 ‖

Pattern 3: 2/4 ♩ 𝄽 | ♩ 𝄽 ‖

The rhythm of the melody is set by the way you say the words.

Step 7: Putting it all together.
It is time to put your composition together. Copy all your choices on the next page. Write the tempo at the beginning of the song. Write the dynamics at the beginning of the song and wherever else they change.

Put the notes on the staff, or just copy the letter names above the words again. If you wish to write the song in music notation, the correct rhythms for the text are above each syllable. The pitches in the song are at the top of the page.

Try performing your composition. Get some friends to play the accompaniment patterns and the harmony. Share your composition with others.

Challenge Try using these tools from the composer's toolbox to create other compositions!

Name ____________________

RESOURCE MASTER 5•7 Practice

Page 7

Pitches in the song:

There's Music in a Hammer

Music by ____________________

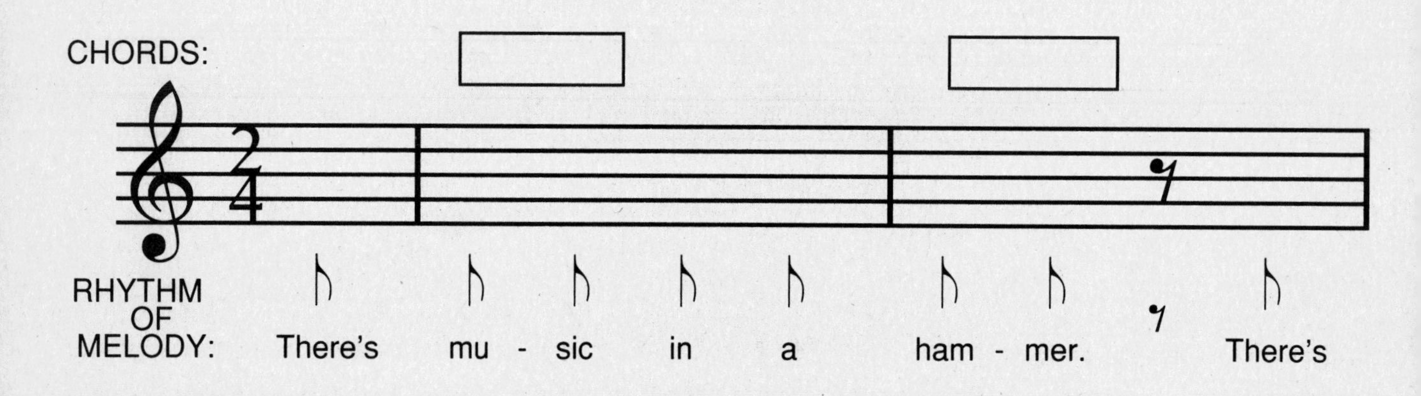

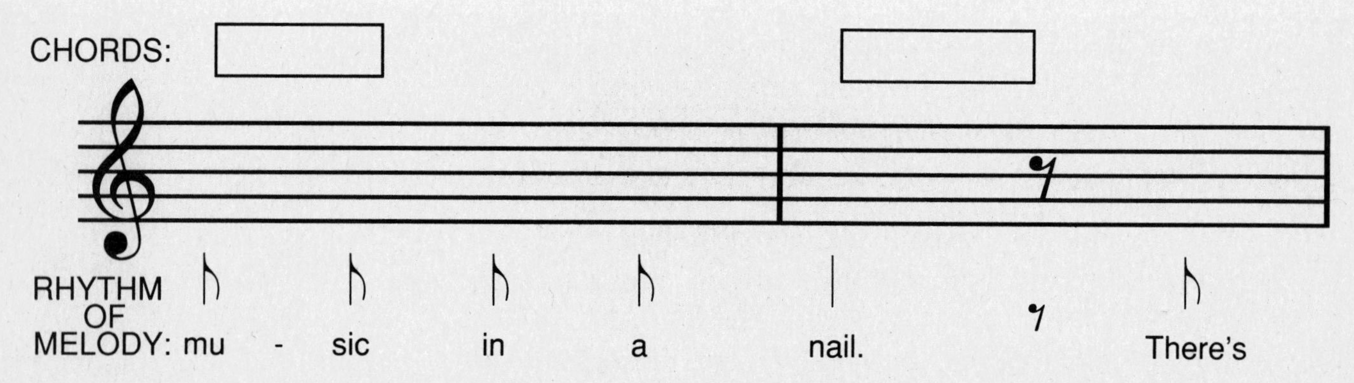

Name ______________________________

Page 8

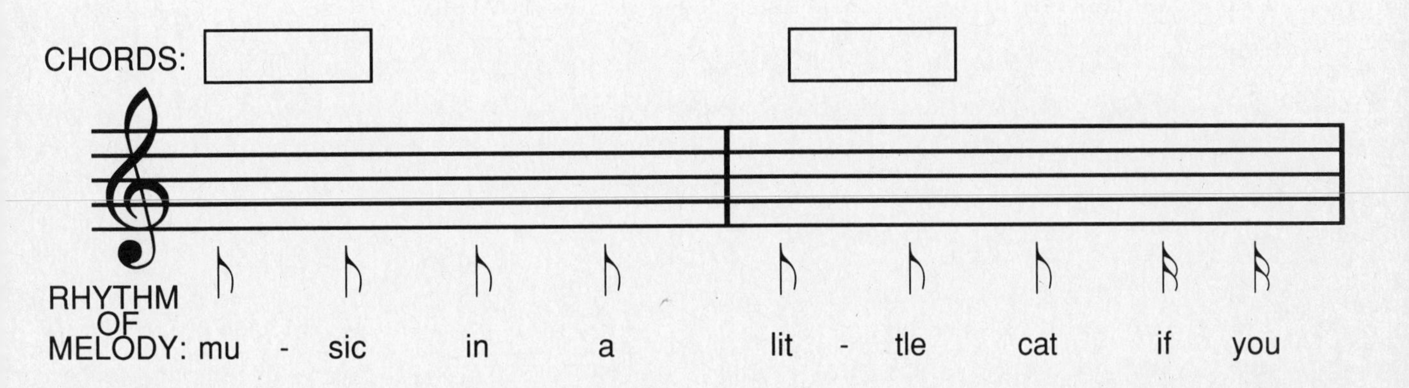

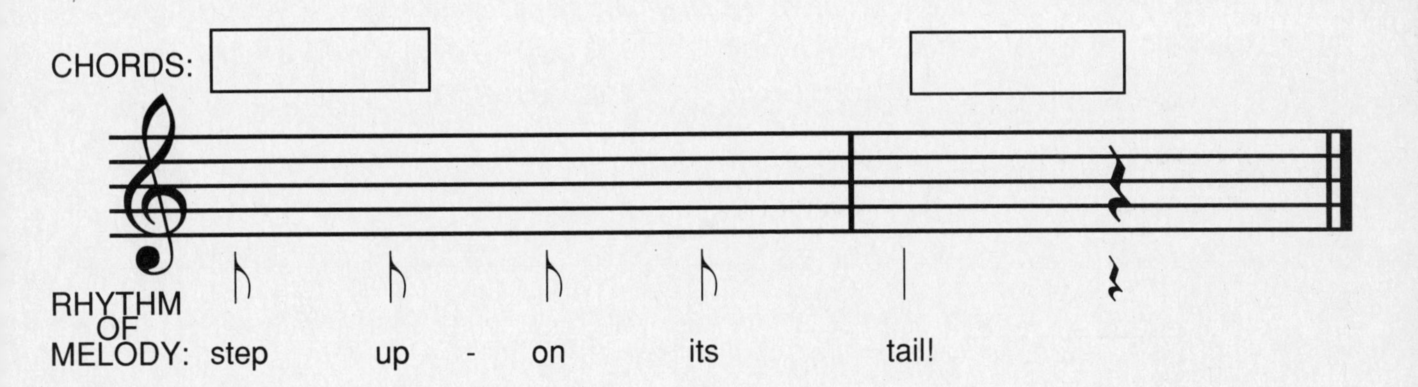

Accompaniment patterns and instrumentation:

Instrument ______________________ Pattern ______________________

Instrument ______________________ Pattern ______________________

Instrument ______________________ Pattern ______________________

Instrument ______________________ Pattern ______________________

Name ______________________________

RESOURCE MASTER 5•8 Assessment

Check It Out

1. Which vocal range do you hear?

a. soprano

c. tenor

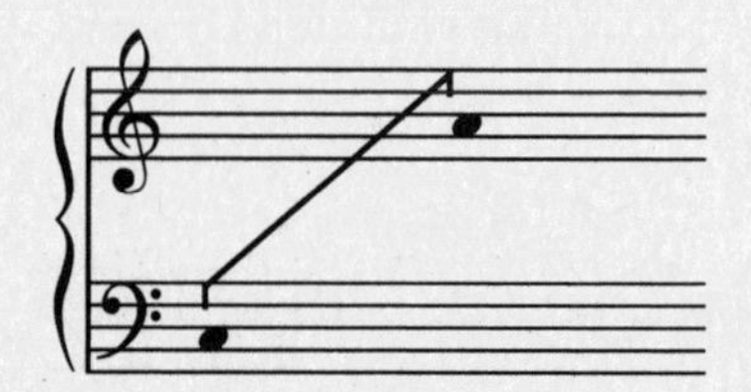

b. alto

d. bass

2. Which musical element is changed?

a. tempo
b. dynamics
c. vocal tone color
d. articulation

3. Which vocal tone color do you hear?

a. heavier voice
b. lighter voice

4. Which articulation do you hear?

a. legato
b. marcato
c. something else

Name ____

Word Puzzle: The 1900s and 1910s

Listen to "A Sound Capsule: 1900s and 1910s." Then write the answer to each clue after its number in the puzzle. Some of the letters are filled in for you. The circled letters will spell a popular music in the 1900s and 1910s.

VOTES FOR WOMEN
1919

1. ___ ___ ___ ___
2. ___ ___ ___ ___ ___ ___ I
3. ___ ___ ___
4. ___ ___ ___ ___ T
5. ___ ___ ___ ___ ___ ___
6. ___ ___ ___ ___ D ___ ___ ___ ___
7. A E R O ___ ___ ___ ___ ___

Clues

1. Produced automobiles by assembly line
2. Sent first radio message through the air
3. "Palm Leaf ______"
4. Popular ragtime composer, ______ Joplin
5. Composed "Alexander's Ragtime Band," Irving ______
6. Change to the Constitution of the United States that must be passed by Congress
7. Wright Brothers' invention

AEROPLANE FLIES
1903

Challenge

Name two songs from the 1900s and 1910s. ____________

____

Begin a book called *From Rag to Rap.* This Resource Master will be page 1. As the unit progresses, add a page for each decade of the twentieth century. If you wish, make a collage of pictures or illustrations for the decade on the back of the Resource Master.

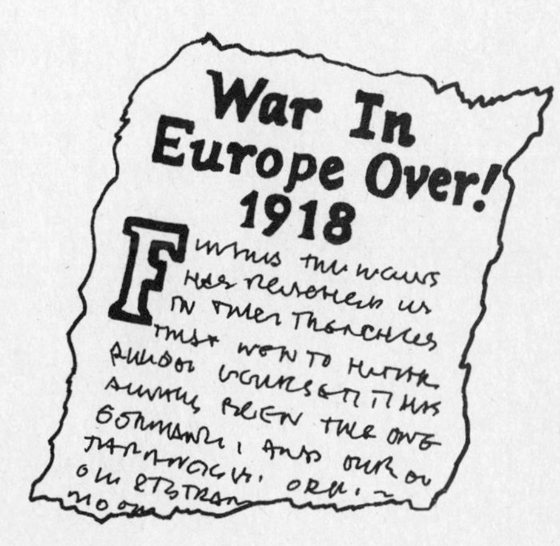

Name ____________________

RESOURCE MASTER 6•2 Practice

The Twenties Test

Listen to "A Sound Capsule: The 1920s." Then circle the events below that happened during the 1920s.

stock-market crash

Russian Revolution ends

first man on the moon

discovery of penicillin

Amelia Earhart flies across Atlantic

invention of telephone

World War I

Running Wild popularizes the Charleston

World War II

invention of television

first television stations established

invention of computers

Vietnam War

Challenge

Name a song from the 1920s.

____

Add Resource Master 6•2 to your book, *From Rag to Rap*.

Name ____

Unscramble The 1930s

Listen to "A Sound Capsule: The 1930s." Then unscramble the letters to answer each question.

1. What film featured Greta Garbo and John Barrymore?

___ ___ ___ ___ ___   ___ ___ ___ ___ ___
D R A N G   T H E L O

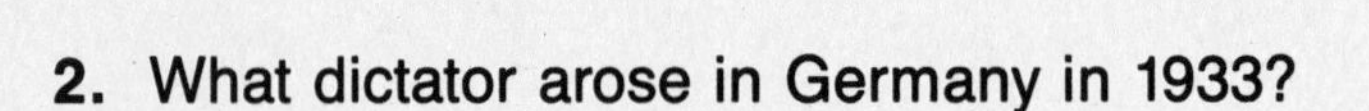

2. What dictator arose in Germany in 1933?

___ ___ ___ ___ ___ ___
R E I T L H

3. What invention made it possible to fly from the Atlantic coast to the Pacific coast in under five hours?

___ ___ ___   ___ ___ ___ ___ ___ ___
T E J   N E N E G I

4. What program did Franklin D. Roosevelt start to provide jobs for the unemployed during the 1930s?

___ ___ ___
W A P

5. What helped connect the rural parts of Africa to the cities in 1931?

___ ___ ___ ___ ___ ___ ___ ___
D R O A L A I R

6. What country did Japan invade in 1937?

___ ___ ___ ___ ___
N A C H I

Challenge

Name two songs from the 1930s. ____

____

Add Resource Master 6•3 to your book, *From Rag to Rap.*

Name ____________________

RESOURCE MASTER 6•4 Practice

Facts of the Forties

You have been chosen to compete in the Quiz Wiz Show. The category today is Facts of the Forties.

Listen to "A Sound Capsule: The 1940s." Then match each item in the left column with the correct person(s) in the right column. Write the letter on the line. If all your answers are correct, you're today's Quiz Wiz!

____ **1.** "The Lincoln Portrait"
____ **2.** *Oklahoma*
____ **3.** *This I Remember*
____ **4.** Made speech declaring war on Japan
____ **5.** 1st African American in major-league baseball

a. Rodgers and Hammerstein
b. Jackie Robinson
c. Franklin D. Roosevelt
d. Eleanor Roosevelt
e. Aaron Copland

Bonus Point
Unscramble the letters in each word to answer the question.

What American naval base did Japan attack in 1941?

__ __ __ __ __   __ __ __ __ __ __
R A P E L   B R O R H A

Add Resource Master 6•4 to your book, *From Rag to Rap*.

Name ______________________________

Word Puzzle: The 1950s

Listen to "A Sound Capsule: The 1950s." Then write the answer to each clue after its number in the puzzle. Some of the letters are filled in for you. The circled letters will spell a popular music in the 1950s.

1. ___ E ___ ___ ___ ___ E I ___
2. ___ O ___ ___ H E I ___
3. ___ C ___ ___ ___ ___ ___ Y
4. ___ I ___ ___
5. ___ P ___ ___ ___ ___ K
6. F ___ A ___ ___
7. W ___ ___ ___ ___ ___
8. ___ ___ ___ ___ E ___
9. ___ A ___ ___ W I ___

Clues

1. Composer of the musical *West Side Story*, a retelling of Shakespeare's *Romeo and Juliet*
2. Lyricist for *West Side Story*
3. Senator who attacked those he suspected of being Communist
4. A leader of the civil-rights movement
5. First satellite to circle the earth, launched by the Soviet Union
6. Jewish teenager who kept a diary as her family hid from the Nazis
7. Composer of the musical *The Music Man*
8. Playwright who wrote *The Crucible*, a play about the Salem witch trials
9. Author of *Notes of a Native Son*, a book about being an African American

Challenge

Choose two events from the 1950s. Write the year(s) they happened. ______________________________

____

Add Resource Master 6•5 to your book, *From Rag to Rap*.

Name ____________________

RESOURCE MASTER 6•6 Practice

The Sixties Scene

Listen to "A Sound Capsule: The 1960s." Then circle the events below that happened during the 1960s.

"The Twist" dance craze

Silent Spring by Rachel Carson

World War II

Richard Nixon resigns presidency

Korean War

Martin Luther King, Jr., assassinated

President John F. Kennedy assassinated

Richard Nixon elected president

Sputnik satellite launch

Vietnam War

anti-war protests sweep U.S.A.

first successful heart transplant

stock-market crash

invention of television

first person walks on the moon

Challenge

Name two songs from the 1960s. ____________________

____

Add Resource Master 6•6 to your book, *From Rag to Rap.*

Name ____________________

Bass Accompaniment and Tablature to "Blowin' in the Wind"

Learn this accompaniment to "Blowin' in the Wind."

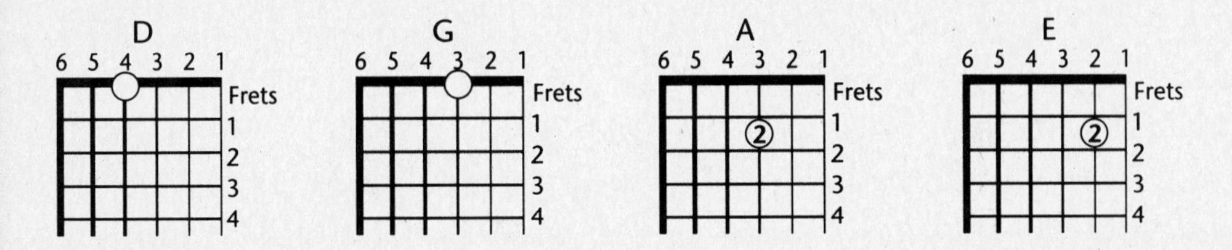

Name ____________________

RESOURCE MASTER 6•8 Practice

The 1970s Name Game

Find and circle these famous names from the 1970s:

Frank Robinson   John Travolta   Hank Aaron   Richard Nixon
Margaret Brewer   Steve Miller   Sarah Caldwell   Mother Teresa

The names may be up, down, across, or diagonal.

R E W E R B T E R A G R A M C O D
B L U V A R T X O P G H S A M L L
O I F T Z T U Q C K P I N D O Y L
P V M S O B L O W Y Z E P F N C E
A F I L T G D O R F P N Y V R A W
C R Y J D E I Z V F K P H I E W D
M A Y E S C V P A A R V K P H U L
L N U D X P N E O M R F H K X D A
V K J B I E U C M L D T R C S D C
Q R I C H A R D N I X O N O X I H
U O H J C I D W E R L B M H P N A
A B M D F A N G M O P L Y L O R R
Y I T D X O K B N Z O T E P M J A
S N I B V O C D E A L D V R U T S
L S N O R A A K N A H P L A D O T
M O T H E R T E R E S A S E P N I
O N F Q U E N O B B I T U V O D A

Add Resource Master 6•8 to your book, *From Rag to Rap*.

Name ____________________

The 1980s Timeline

Listen to "A Sound Capsule: The 1980s." Then fill in the timeline with these events:

- Sally Ride, American woman astronaut, 1983
- home computers introduced, 1981
- Martin Luther King, Jr. Day, becomes law, 1984
- compact discs introduced, 1983
- "Thriller" wins 8 Grammy awards, 1984
- Mount St. Helens erupts, 1980
- Guion Bluford, African American astronaut, 1983
- *Raiders of the Lost Ark*, 1981
- nuclear arms-reduction treaty, 1987
- AZT drug discovered, 1987

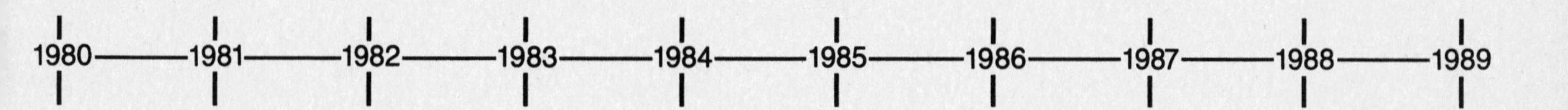

Challenge

Add other events from the 1980s to the timeline.

Add Resource Master 6•9 to your book, *From Rag to Rap*.

Name ____________________

RESOURCE MASTER 6•10 Practice

The 1990s World

The world seems smaller today as ideas and people travel more quickly than ever. Listen to "A Sound Capsule: The 1990s." Then locate these countries in the news on the correct continent of the world map below. Use an atlas if you need help.

Russia Iraq Kuwait Somalia United States Yugoslavia

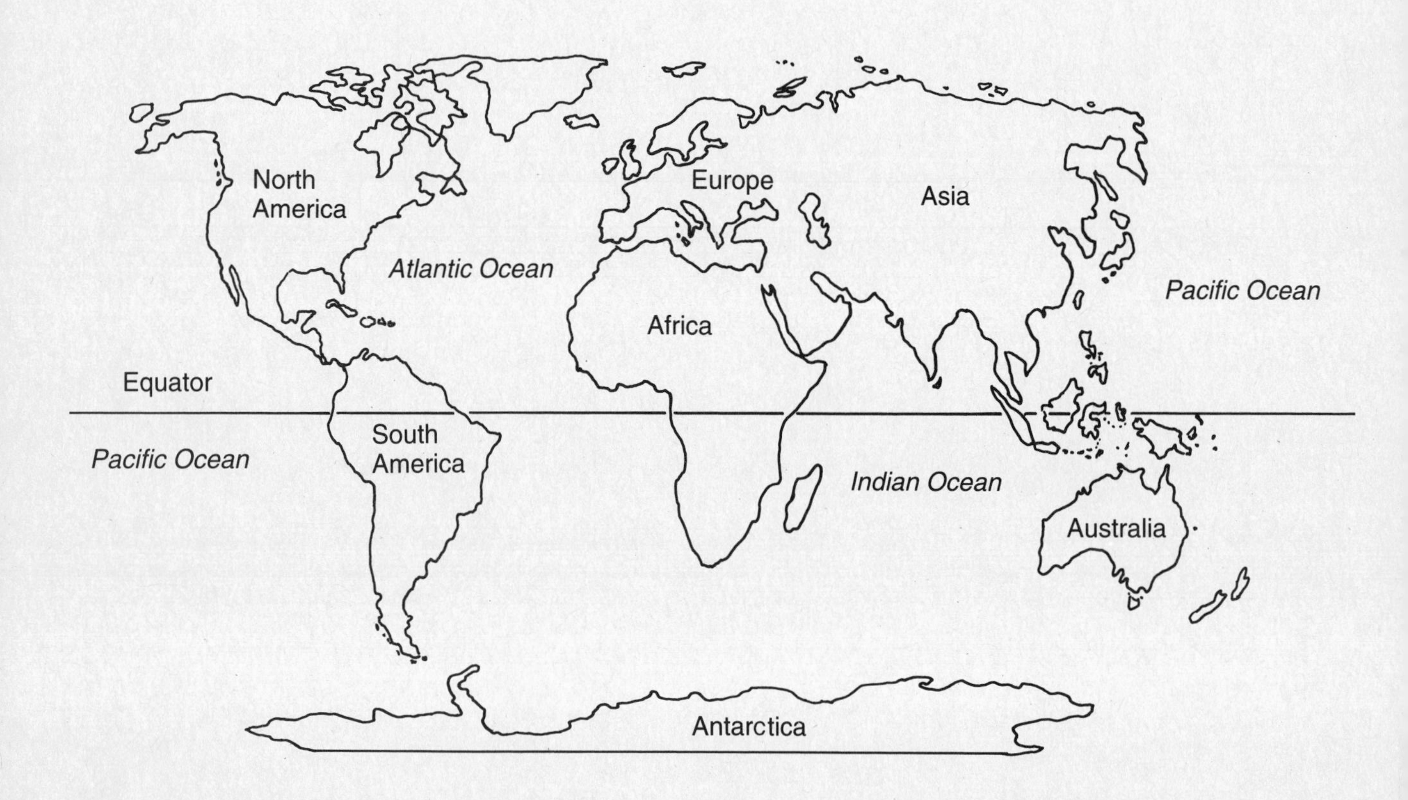

Challenge

Name four songs from the 1990s. ____________________

____

Add Resource Master 6•10 to your book, *From Rag to Rap*. Then make a title page and table of contents page for the entire book. This completes the book, which you can illustrate as you wish.

Name ______________________________

Music Video Script

Song Title ______________________________

Composer ______________________________

Music Group: Write the names of the students who will perform in the music video.

Singers	

Instrumentalists	Instruments

Dancers	

Name ______________________________

RESOURCE MASTER 6•11 Practice

Page 2

This page is to be used by the music group and the script group. The music group is responsible for planning who will sing and play in the music video. The script group writes the script, the description needed for the actors, singers, and musicians to portray the song on the screen.

Music Group: Under the column marked "Audio," the music group should list, in order, all sound to be heard in the music video. List the sections as they occur in the music. Leave some space for the script group to list any sound effects or narration. Write the length of time needed for each section in the column marked "Time." Use extra paper if necessary. Then give this page to the script group.

Script Group: Fill in the column marked "Video" with the sequence of scenes and events that go along with the music. Then add any sound effects or narration, and mark the length of time needed under "Time."

Time	Audio	Video

Name ____________________

Music Video Storyboard

Script Group: Use this form to make a storyboard that shows, in drawings, how each shot in the Music Video Script will look.

Step 1 Draw one picture for each camera shot in the boxes labeled "Drawing." Use stick figures or simple sketches.

Step 2 In the boxes labeled "Camera Shot," describe the type of shot using these symbols:

WS = wide shot MS = medium shot CU = close up
ZI = zoom in ZO = zoom out

Step 3 In the boxes labeled "Audio," write the section of the music (or other sound) that will be used with each shot. Use extra paper if necessary.

Drawing			
Camera Shot			
Audio			

Drawing			
Camera Shot			
Audio			

Name ____________________

RESOURCE MASTER 6•13 Practice

Music Video Shooting Sheet

Script Group: Use this form to summarize each shot in the music video. It will be used to guide the person operating the camera.

Time	Video	Camera Shot	Performers	Action	Audio

To the teacher: Give several copies of Resource Master 6•13 to the script group to compile a running list of the shots for the music video. This list should be an abbreviated version of the information on Resource Master 6•11 and Resource Master 6•12. Have students transfer the information on the Resource Masters to the appropriate columns. In the column labeled "Action," have students describe the actions of the performers in each shot.

Name ___

Battle Hymn of the Republic

played by the Monty Alexander Trio

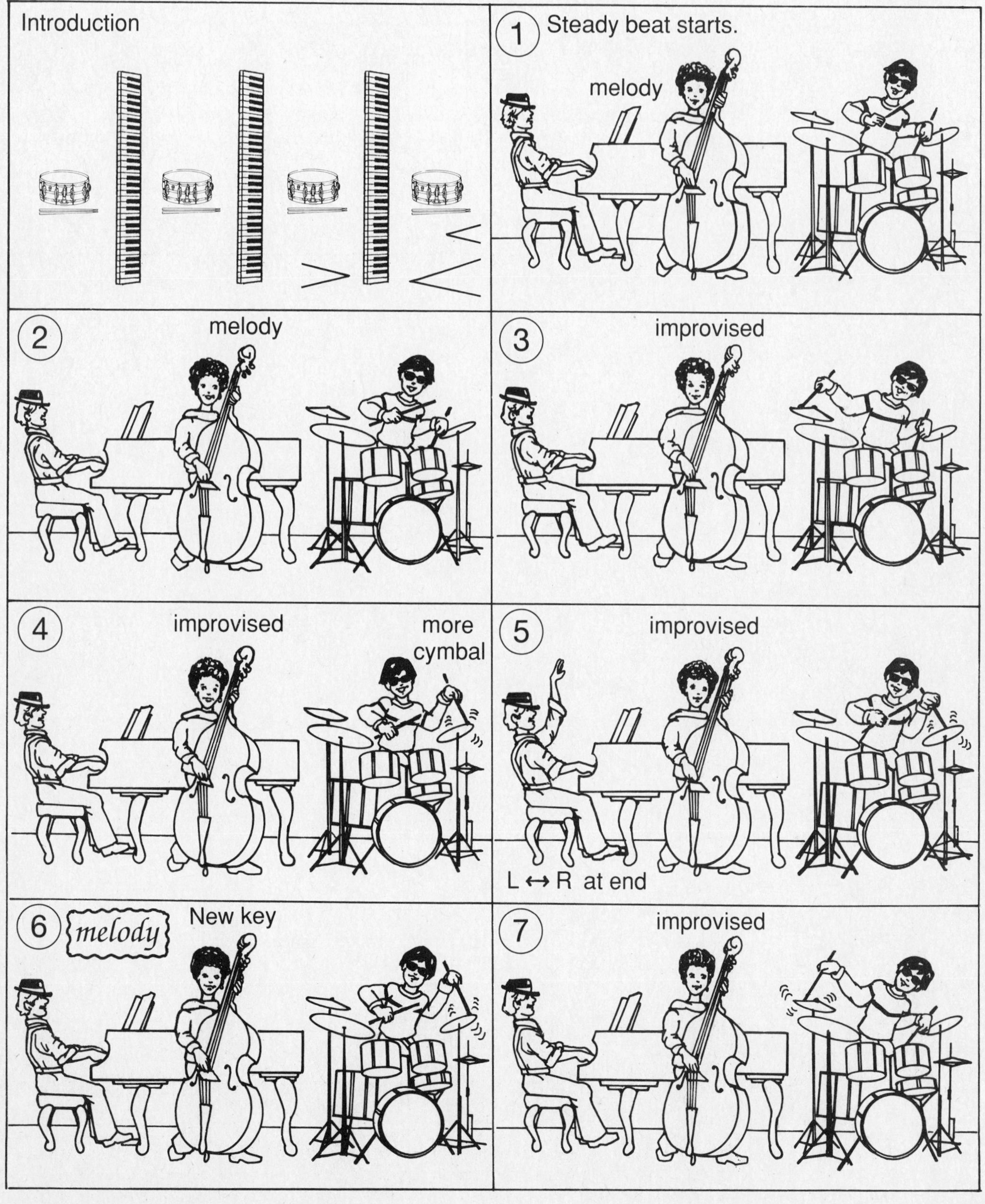

USING RESOURCE MASTER C•1

DIRECTIONS:

Distribute a copy of the Resource Master to each student. Have students identify all instruments on the listening map. (box 1: four snare drums and three piano keyboards; all other boxes: drum set, string bass, piano) Note that the introduction is the only section without a consistent steady beat. Point out that the drummer is concentrating on playing the cymbals in boxes 4, 5, 6, and 7. Students should listen for this when you play the recording. Have students find boxes with the label *melody* (boxes 1, 2, and 6) and those with the label *improvised* (boxes 3, 4, 5, and 7). Review the meaning of *improvised* if necessary.

Name ____________________

Lyrics: "Holiday Sing-Along"

Deck the Hall

Deck the hall with boughs of holly,
Fa la la la la, la la la la,
'Tis the season to be jolly,
Fa la la la la, la la la la,
Don we now our gay apparel,
Fa la la, la la la, la la la,
Troll the ancient yuletide carol
Fa la la la la, la la la la.

We Three Kings

We three kings of Orient are,
Bearing gifts we traverse afar,
Field and fountain, moor and mountain,
Following yonder star.
O Star of wonder, star of night,
Star with royal beauty bright,
Westward leading, still proceeding,
Guide us to thy perfect light.

The Holly and the Ivy

The holly and the ivy,
When they are both full grown,
Of all the trees that are in the wood,
The holly bears the crown.
The rising of the sun
And the running of the deer,
The playing of the merry organ,
Sweet singing in the choir.

Angels We Have Heard on High

Angels we have heard on high,
sweetly singing o'er the plains,
And the mountains in reply
echoing their joyous strains;
Gloria in excelsis Deo,
Gloria in excelsis Deo.

Name ____________________

RESOURCE MASTER C•2 Text

Page 2

God Rest Ye Merry, Gentlemen

God rest ye merry, gentlemen,
Let nothing you dismay,
Remember Christ our Savior
Was born on Christmas Day;
To save us all from Satan's power
When we were gone astray.

Refrain
O tidings of comfort and joy, comfort
and joy,
O tidings of comfort and joy.

From God, our heav'nly Father,
A blessed Angel came;
And unto certain shepherds,
Brought tidings of the same:
How that in Bethlehem was born,
The Son of God by name.

Refrain

Joy to the World

Joy to the world! the Lord is come;
Let earth receive her King;
Let ev'ry heart prepare Him room.
And heav'n and nature sing,
And heav'n and nature sing,
And heav'n, and heav'n and nature sing.

Silent Night

Silent night, holy night,
All is calm, all is bright
Round yon Virgin Mother and Child.
Holy Infant so tender and mild,
Sleep in heavenly peace,
Sleep in heavenly peace.

Wasn't That a Mighty Day?

Wasn't that a mighty day?
Hallelu, Hallelu,
Wasn't that a mighty day
when Jesus Christ was born?
Well, Jesus was a baby
a lyin' at Mary's arm,
Lyin' in the stable at Bethlehem,
the beasts they keep-a him warm.

We Wish You a Merry Christmas

We wish you a merry Christmas,
We wish you a merry Christmas,
We wish you a merry Christmas,
And a happy New Year.

Refrain
Good tidings we bring to you and your kin,
Good tidings for Christmas and a happy
New Year.

Now bring us some figgy pudding,
Now bring us some figgy pudding,
Now bring us some figgy pudding,
And bring it out here.

Refrain

We wish you a merry Christmas,
We wish you a merry Christmas,
We wish you a merry Christmas,
And a Happy New Year.

Name ____

Playalong: Música indígena

Clap the rhythm as you listen to "Música indígena."

Music by Manuel María Ponce
Playalong by Robert S. de Frece

Name ______________________________

RESOURCE MASTER RA•1 Practice

Vocal Accompaniment Parts: "Every Mornin' When I Wake Up"

Add an introduction to "Every Mornin' When I Wake Up." Begin by singing Part 5. Then add Parts 4, 3, 2, and 1 in order every four measures. The parts can continue throughout the song. For a coda, stop the parts one at a time.

Arranged by Avon Gillespie
Adapted by Marilyn Davidson

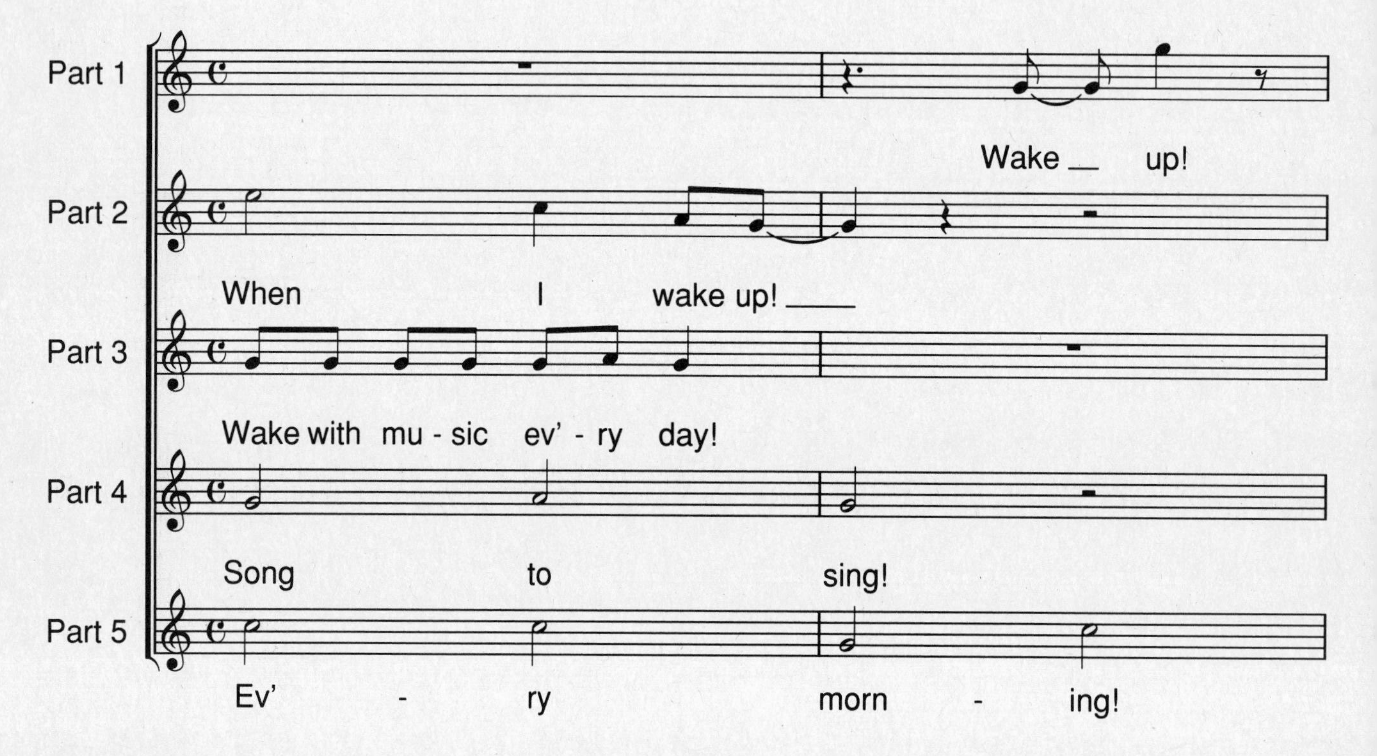

Name ____________________

Page 2

Part 1
My chil - dren
Part 2
When I wake up!
Part 3
Wake with mu - sic ev' - ry day!
Part 4
Song to sing!
Part 5
Ev' - ry morn - ing!

Name ____________________

RESOURCE MASTER RA•2 Practice

Playalong: "I Got a Letter"

Name ____________________

Playalong: "De Lanterna na Mão"

Instrumental part by Marilyn Davidson

Name ____________________

RESOURCE MASTER SA•1 Practice

Accompaniment Parts: "Island in the Sun"

Clap the rhythm and speak the chant for each instrument.

(Verses only)

Cowbell

is - land

Bongos

man-y a sea

Claves

your shin-ing sand

Güiro

(ca) lyp - so with ca -

(Refrain only)

Maracas

Play the instruments as you speak the chant again. Then use the instruments as you sing "Island in the Sun."

Name ____________________

Percussion: "El zapatero"

Arranged by
Carl S.Miller

Introduction

(Voice enters on 4th time)

COWBELL mf mf 11 TIMBALES (CONGA DRUM) mf 7

WOOD BLOCK

MARACAS mf 11 7

(C.B.) mp mp 3

(W.Bl.)

(Mar.) mp 3

(Timb.) p 2 cresc. f

(C.B.) mf mf mp 10 mp

(W.Bl)

(Mar.) mf 10 mp

(Timb.) mf 3 cresc.

(W.Bl.) f

(Timb.) f

Name ______________________________

RESOURCE MASTER CA•2 Practice

Bongos: "Keep Your Lamps!"

Bongos Accompaniment
by Judy Bond

Name ______________________________

Jubilate Deo

by Giovanni Gabrieli

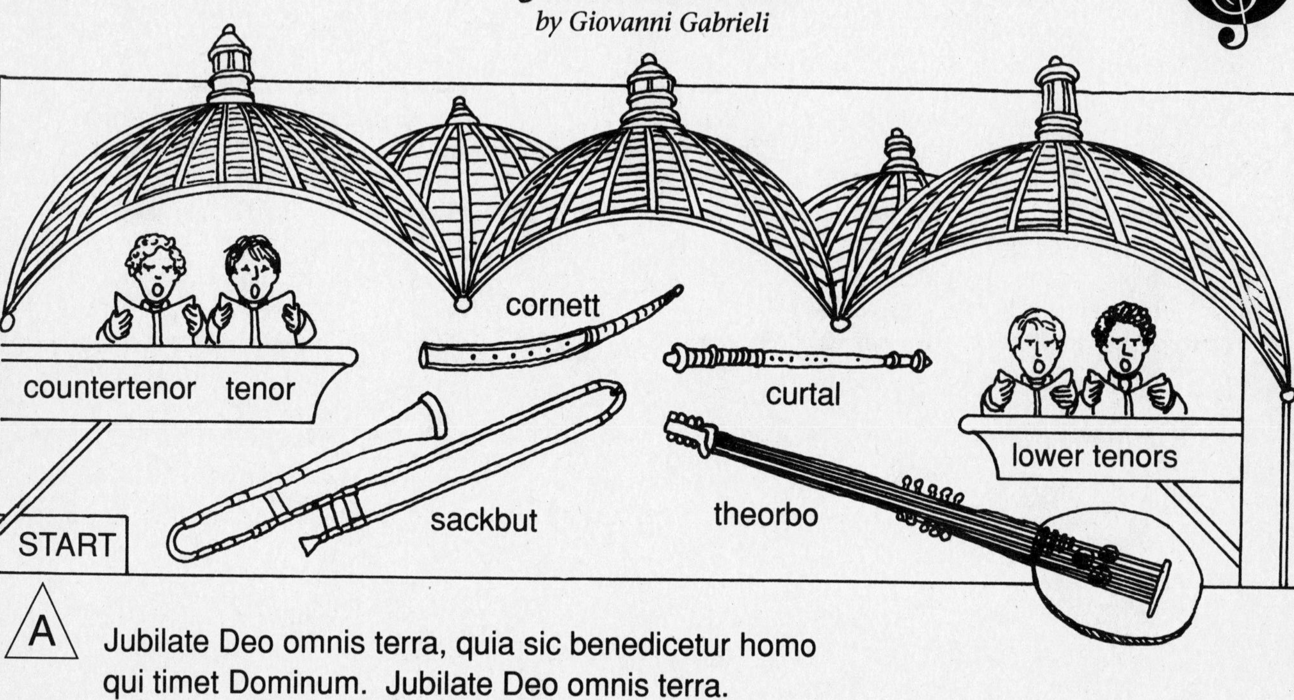

A — Jubilate Deo omnis terra, quia sic benedicetur homo qui timet Dominum. Jubilate Deo omnis terra.

B — (0:41)

Deus | Deus Israel | Deus Israel | conjugat | conjugat | conjugat | conjugat...

Et ipse | Et ipse | Et ipse sic vobiscum | sic vobiscum... | ☐ | ☐ | ☐ | ☐

Mit - ⁓⁓⁓ tat vobis. | Auxilium | Auxilium | de sancto, et de Sion tueatur vos,

tueatur vos | et de Sion | et de Sion | tueatur vos | tueatur vos. | Jubilate

Deo om - ⁓⁓ nis ter - ⁓⁓ ra.

(2:15)

C — Benedicat vobis Dominus ex Sion, qui fecit caelum et terram. Jubilate Deo omnis terra.

D — (3:16)

Servite Domino in laetitia.

USING RESOURCE MASTER LA•1

DIRECTIONS:

Distribute a copy of the Resource Master to each student. Have students identify the one singer at the top of the listening map who is not a tenor. (the countertenor, located at the far left) Help students identify the instruments pictured on the map. (sackbut, cornett, curtal, and theorbo) Explain each instrument using information in the Teacher's Edition. Point out the *A, B, C,* and *D* sections on the map and explain that there is an echo, or antiphonal, effect in many parts of this selection; this effect is illustrated in the B section, where it is most clearly heard. You may wish to have students color the singers' balcony and music books on the left side red and those on the right side (lower tenors) blue, and color the upper text boxes of rows in the B section red and the lower text boxes blue, to help clarify which range voices are singing when. (See Listening Map Transparency T•11.)

Name ________________________________

Symphony No. 5 in C Minor Op. 67, First Movement

by Ludwig van Beethoven

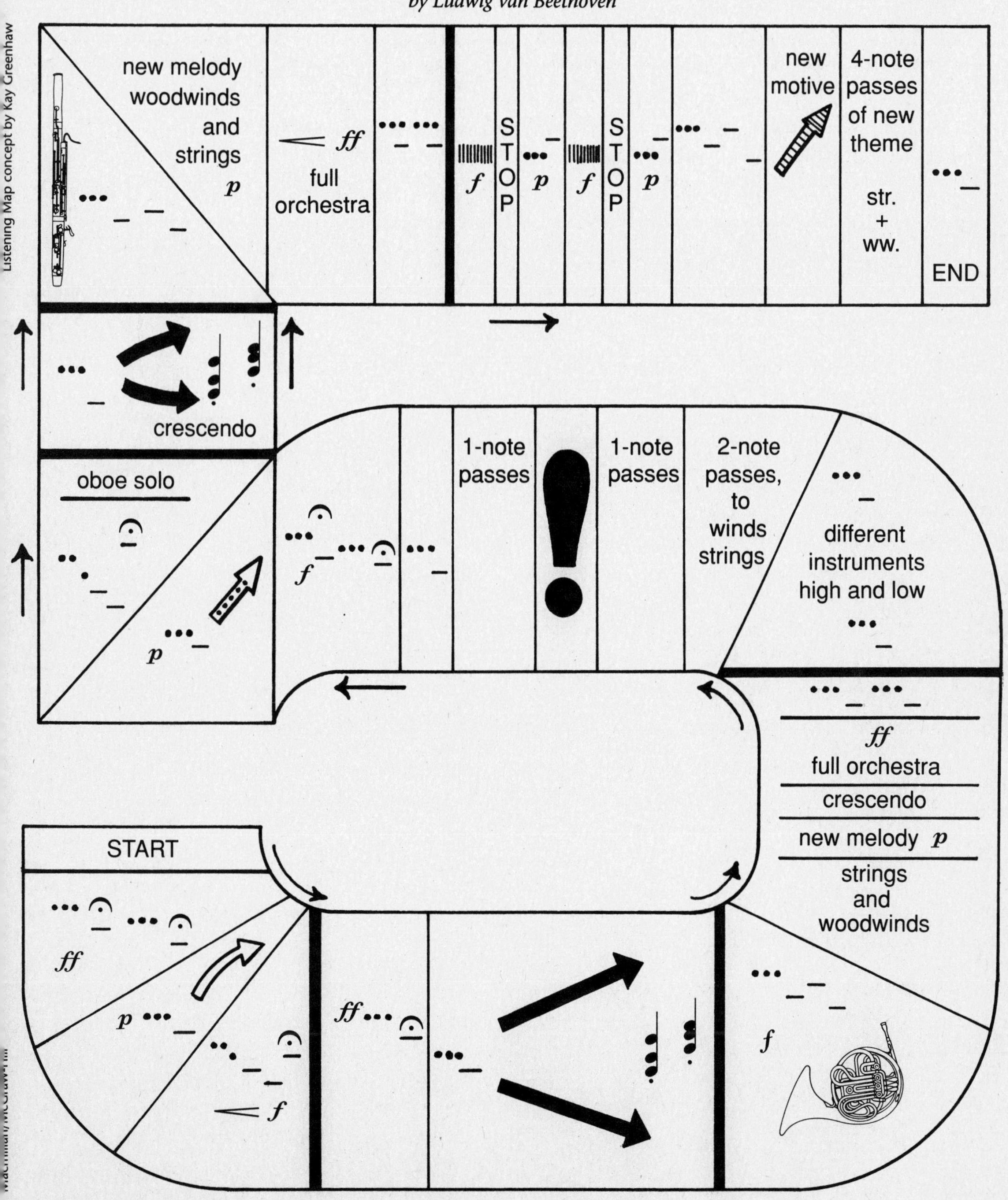

USING RESOURCE MASTER LA•2

DIRECTIONS:

Distribute a copy of the Resource Master to each student. Tell students that they are to start at the bottom of the numeral *5* and work their way up to the top. Have students identify the two instruments pictured on the map. (French horn and bassoon) Explain that the symbols "dot-dot-dot-line" represent the recurring four-note motive of this movement. Sometimes one appearance of the motive stands for several repetitions. You may wish to play this motive as printed in the Teacher's Edition Theme area on a pitched instrument before the first listening.

Name ______________________________

Ride of the Valkyries from *Die Walküre*

by Richard Wagner

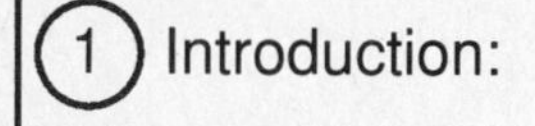

fluttering
woodwinds
and strings

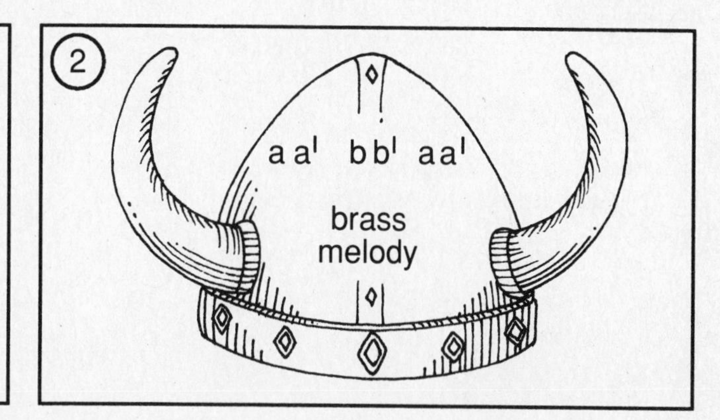

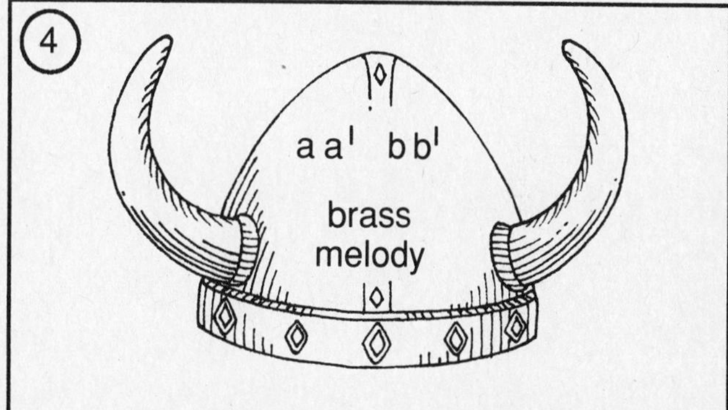

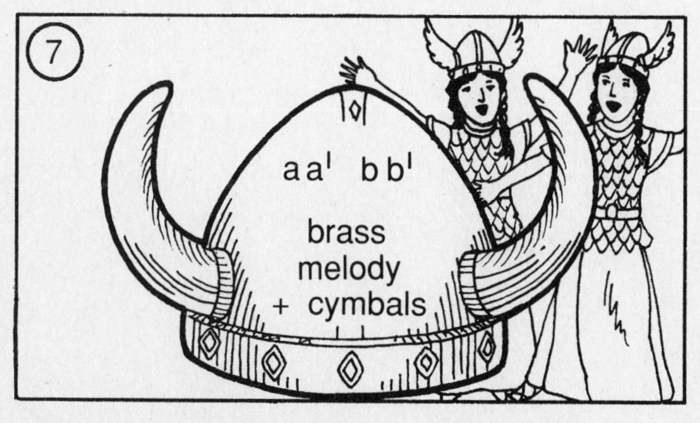

USING RESOURCE MASTER LA•3

DIRECTIONS:

Distribute a copy of the Resource Master to each student. Point out the phrase indications (*a, a', b,* or *b'*) on each helmet. The themes are heard in these places; other boxes indicate contrasting melodic material. Point out that sometimes the women sing these theme phrases, and sometimes they sing contrasting material. The helmet in box 7 has bolder lines because it is louder and in a major key. In box 7 the women are singing together and are heard late during that box, so they are located toward the right. See the Teacher's Edition for an explanation of the story and a summary of the text sung.

Name ______________________________

Seventeen Come Sunday
from *English Folk Song Suite*

by Ralph Vaughan Williams

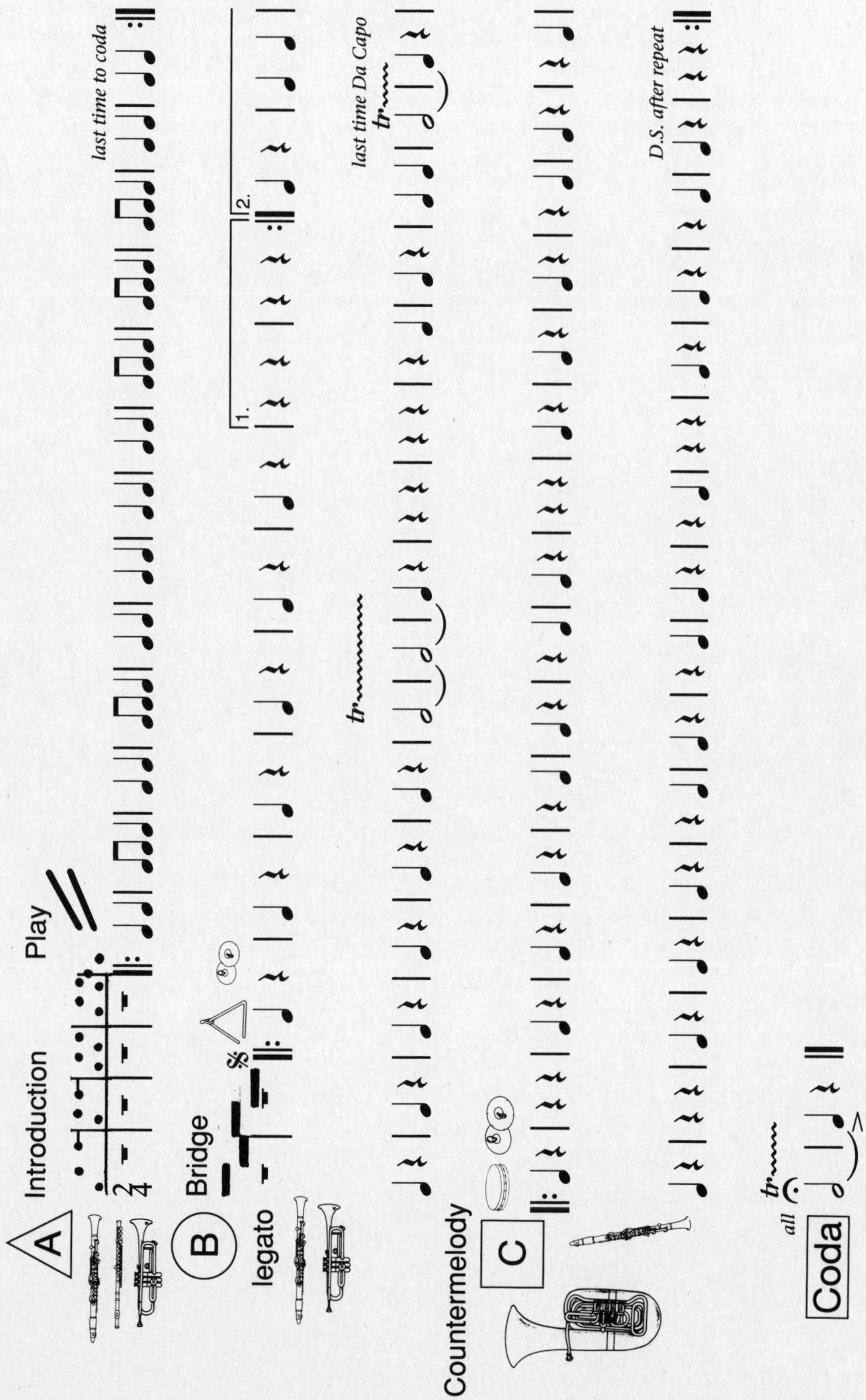
A
Introduction
Play
last time to coda
B
Bridge
legato
1.
2.
last time Da Capo
tr
Countermelody
C
D.S. after repeat
all
tr
Coda

Listening Map concept by Debbie Tannert

USING RESOURCE MASTER LA•4

DIRECTIONS:

Distribute a copy of the Resource Master to each student. Have students identify each instrument pictured on the map. (clarinet, flute, trumpet below the A label, rhythm sticks just after the introduction; clarinet and trumpet below the B label, triangle and finger cymbals to the right of the B label; tuba and clarinet below the C label, hand drum and crash cymbals to the right of the C label)

Explain that the instruments below the section labels are instruments heard in those sections, and instruments pictured to the right of section labels are instruments students are to play. Point out the repeat signs, the *D. S.* indication, the coda, and all other directives on the map before listening to or playing with the recording.

Name ____

Concerto for Orchestra, Second Movement ("Game of Pairs")

by Béla Bartók

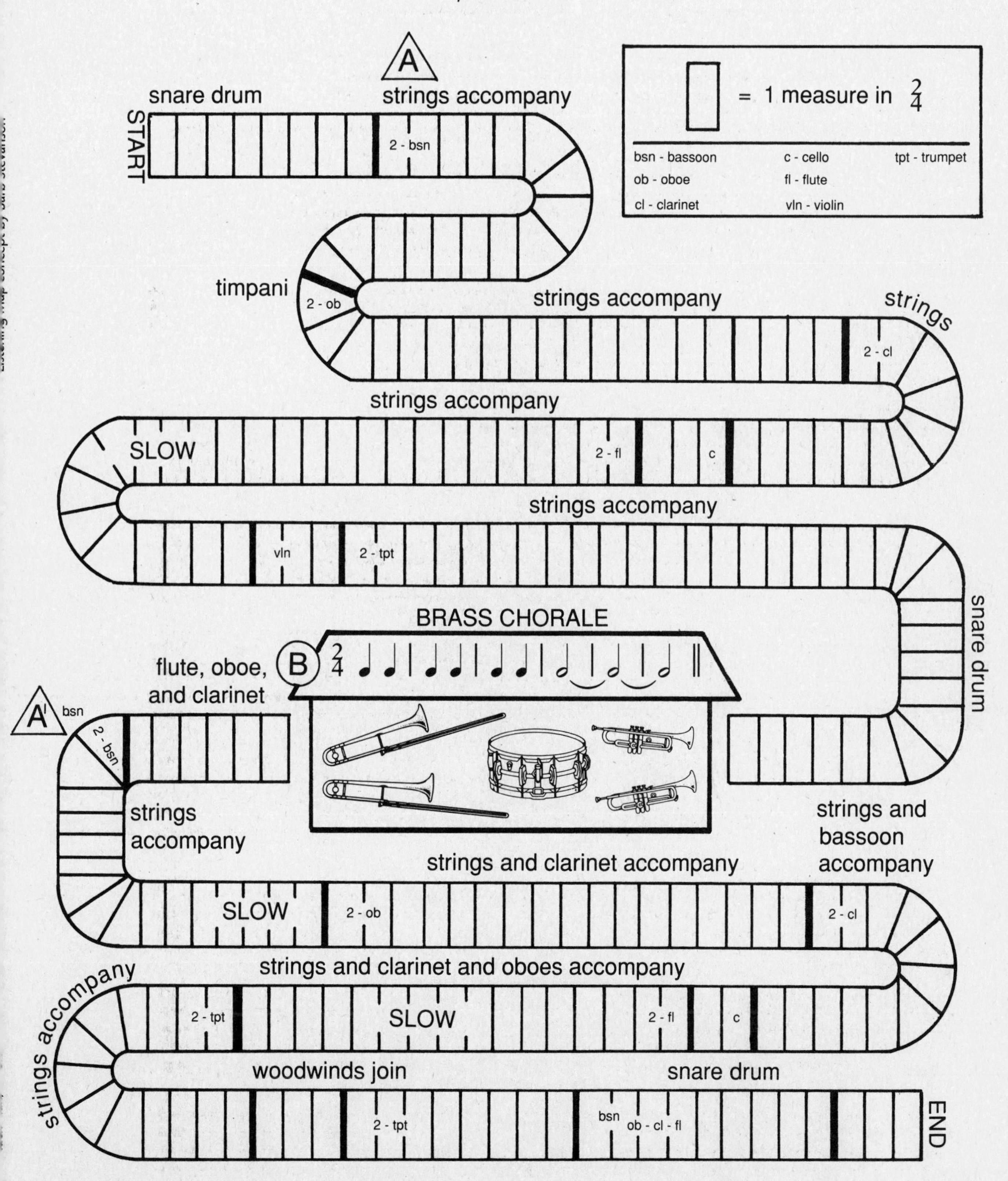

USING RESOURCE MASTER LA•5

DIRECTIONS:

Distribute a copy of the Resource Master to each student. Point out the *A, B* and *A'* sections on the map. Note that each square on the pathway represents one measure containing two beats. After examining the key, have students identify each instrument abbreviation on the path (snare drum, bassoons, oboes, clarinets, cello, flutes, violin, and trumpets), and those listed off the path as accompaniment instruments. Point out the three places on the pathway where the beat slows down.

Name ____

Amoeba

by Judith E. Ficksman

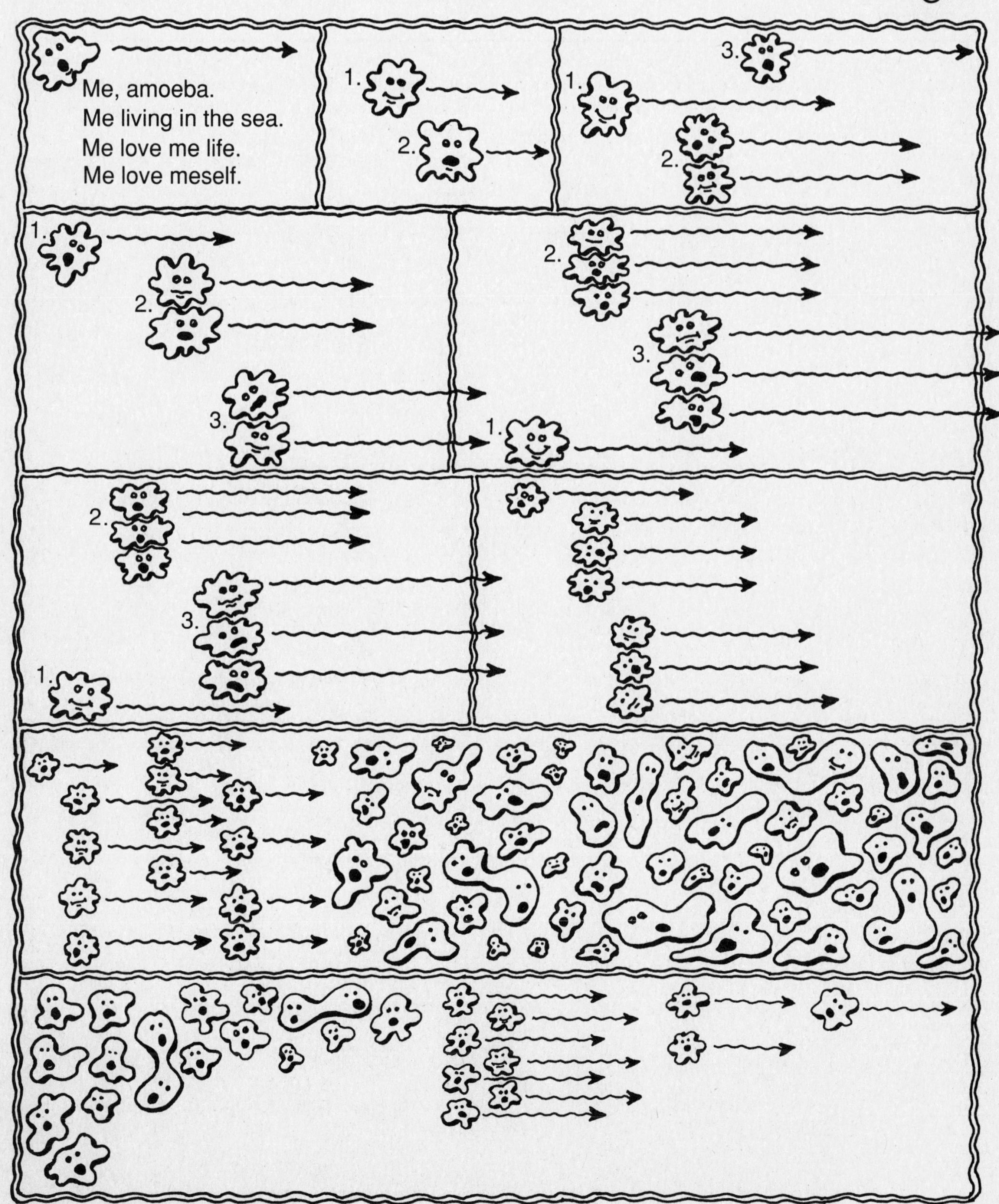

USING RESOURCE MASTER LA•6

DIRECTIONS:

Distribute a copy of the Resource Master to each student. Point out that this selection starts and ends with one voice singing an imagined amoeba's view of life (printed in the first box). The number of amoebas singing this little text increases gradually, as shown on the map. The exact number is not shown, just the indication of one or more than one. The relative pitch of each group entry is shown within each box. The penultimate box represents the chaos of the most populated section of this selection. Note that the final groups of amoebas are located at the top of the last box. This shows the relatively high final pitch levels.

Name ____________________

Earth Kids

A Musical for Our World

Music by Neil Fishman   Book and lyrics by Harvey Edelman
Story conceived by Harvey and Julie Edelman
Script adapted by Nancy Miller

CAST

Natural Resources*

Air 1	**Forest 1**
Air 2	**Forest 2**
Air 3	**Forest 3**
River 1	**Forest 4**
River 2	**Forest 5**
Fossil Fuel 1	**Animal 1**
Fossil Fuel 2	**Animal 2**
Fossil Fuel 3	**Animal 3**
Fossil Fuel 4	**Animal 4**
Fossil Fuel 5	**Animal 5**

Kids/Earth Kids

Phyllis, a practical kid
Ian, an idealist
Skip, a skeptical one
Al, always apathetic
Jamie, Al's younger sister (or brother)
New Kid 1
New Kid 2

*An unnumbered Natural Resource in the script means that all of that particular resource will speak the line(s).

Setting: A forest alongside a river
Time: The present. A summer afternoon

Overture: Instrumental version of "Here Come the Earth Kids"

SCENE I The Arrival

(As this scene begins, five kids wearing hiking clothes and day packs are coming down the center aisle of the audience talking and laughing.)

Ian *(running ahead of the others and calling out)*: Hurry up, gang! We're almost there.

Skip: *(Groans).* That's what you said fifteen minutes ago.

Ian: Yeah, but this time it's true. Listen. You can hear the river. *(all stop to listen)*

(Special Effect: flowing water)

Jamie: I *can* hear it! I can't wait to get my feet wet. Hey, Al, I'll race ya to the water.

Al: You'll what? *(starts running with Jamie in pursuit. The two yell and laugh as they run onto the stage and exit stage left.)*

Ian *(arriving on stage and calling after them):* Don't go too far. We're stopping at this clearing. *(to the others)* Well, this is it, guys. What do you think?

Phyllis: This is beautiful, Ian. It's even better than I expected.

Skip: Yeah, Ian. I thought you were exaggerating when you described this spot, but it's just like you said. . .clean and cool.

Phyllis: Look at this, Skip. Moss all over the place.

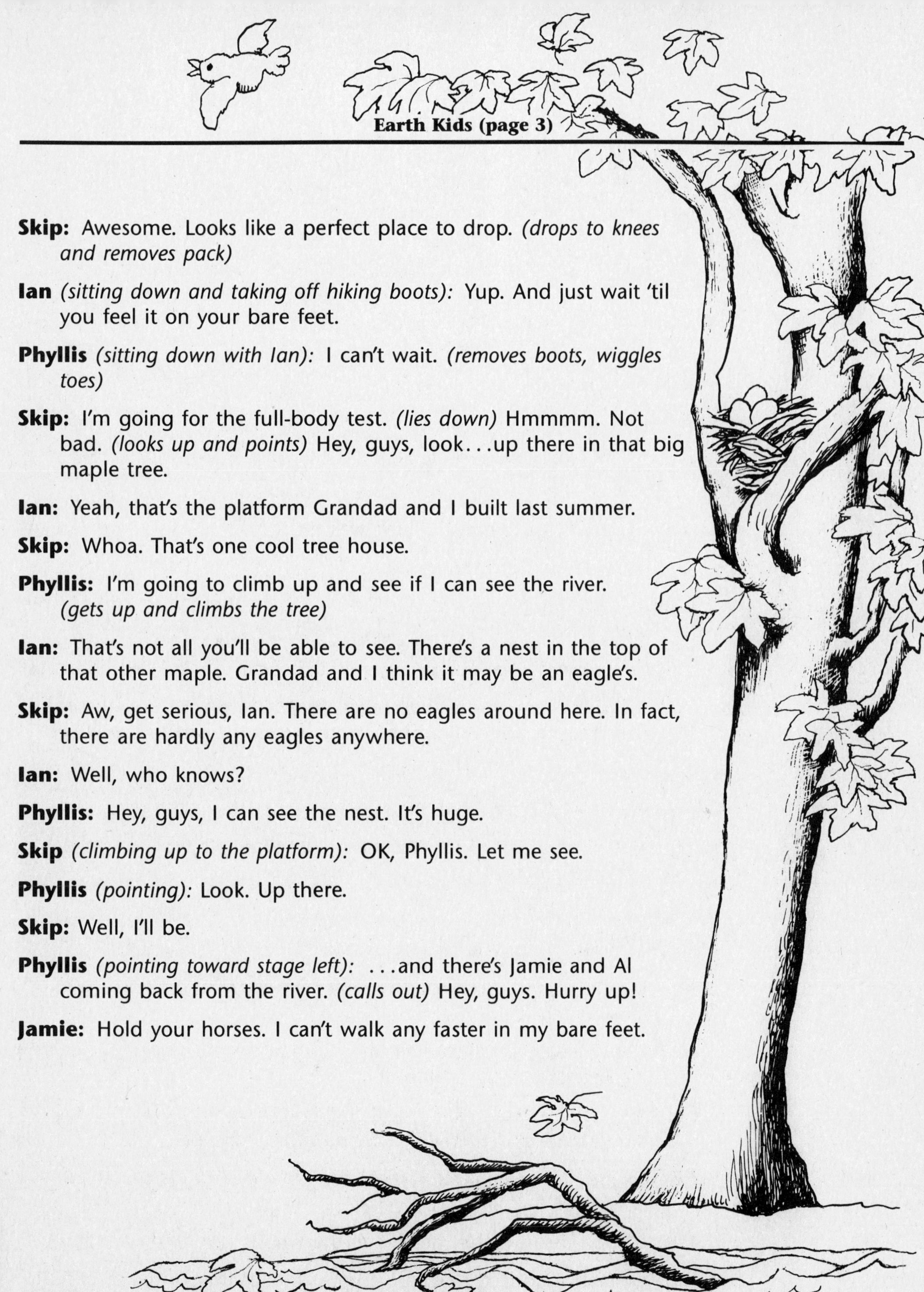

Skip: Awesome. Looks like a perfect place to drop. *(drops to knees and removes pack)*

Ian *(sitting down and taking off hiking boots):* Yup. And just wait 'til you feel it on your bare feet.

Phyllis *(sitting down with Ian):* I can't wait. *(removes boots, wiggles toes)*

Skip: I'm going for the full-body test. *(lies down)* Hmmmm. Not bad. *(looks up and points)* Hey, guys, look. . .up there in that big maple tree.

Ian: Yeah, that's the platform Grandad and I built last summer.

Skip: Whoa. That's one cool tree house.

Phyllis: I'm going to climb up and see if I can see the river. *(gets up and climbs the tree)*

Ian: That's not all you'll be able to see. There's a nest in the top of that other maple. Grandad and I think it may be an eagle's.

Skip: Aw, get serious, Ian. There are no eagles around here. In fact, there are hardly any eagles anywhere.

Ian: Well, who knows?

Phyllis: Hey, guys, I can see the nest. It's huge.

Skip *(climbing up to the platform):* OK, Phyllis. Let me see.

Phyllis *(pointing):* Look. Up there.

Skip: Well, I'll be.

Phyllis *(pointing toward stage left):* . . .and there's Jamie and Al coming back from the river. *(calls out)* Hey, guys. Hurry up!

Jamie: Hold your horses. I can't walk any faster in my bare feet.

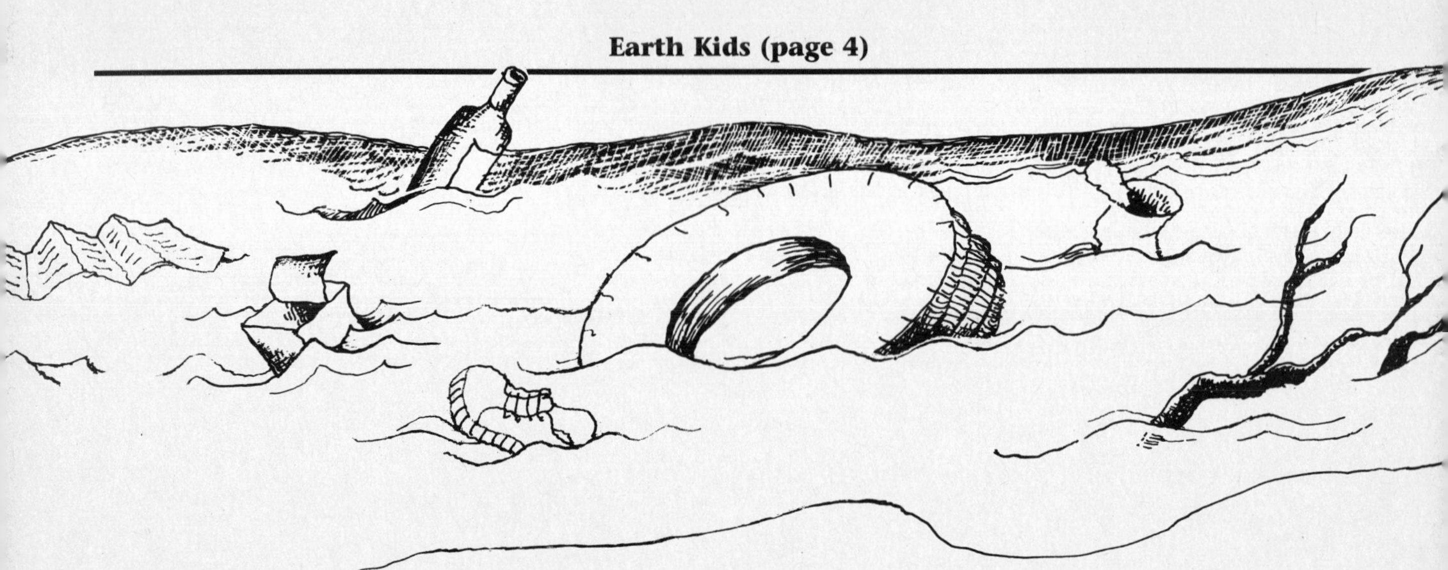

Ian *(as Jamie and Al arrive):* How was the river?

Al: Cold, clear, and running fast.

Jamie: Well, I don't know about the clear part. That river is full of junk.

Ian: Yeah, I know and it gets worse every year. When I was a little kid, the river was great, hardly any stuff in it at all. . .only fallen branches.

Jamie: Well, there's more than fallen branches, now. I pulled three rusty cans, a potato-chip bag, and an old tire out of the water.

Ian: Yuk.

Phyllis: . . .and from here, I can see a whole car in the river.

Jamie *(looking up when she hears Phyllis's voice):* Phyllis! How did you get up there?

Phyllis: Climbed.

Skip: Come on up, you two. It's great.

Al: Not me. *(opens day pack and takes out food)* I'm taking care of my stomach first.

Ian: Good idea, Al. I'm starved after all that hiking. *(takes food out of day pack and starts to eat)*

(All kids talk about eating as they find a place to sit and get out their food. Skip and Phyllis come down from the tree.)

Phyllis: So, tell us, Ian. How come this little clearing is so. . .well, so forest-like?

Ian: . . .you mean when the rest of the woods is more like a dump?

Jamie: Yeah, I noticed that, too. There's lots of trash around, except for this spot.

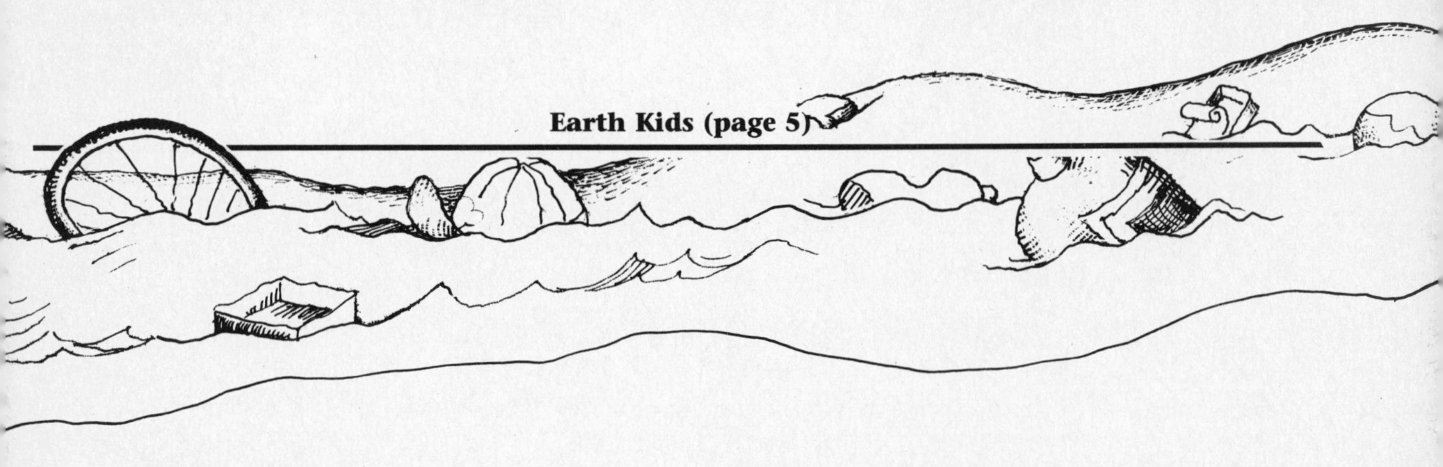

Ian: Well, you see Grandad and I have been coming to this very spot ever since I was four, and we always clean up whatever trash we find here and take it to a real dump.

Al: You mean, you actually haul trash out of the woods?

Ian: Sure.

Al: Why go to all that trouble? You could just heave it into the underbrush. Look. *(throws soda can toward the river)*

Jamie *(disgusted):* Al...Why did you do that? Soda cans are recyclable.

Al: Well, excuuuuse me! *(picks up another one and throws it)*

Jamie *(rushing over and pounding on him):* Al Cartright, you are the laziest, most ornery...

Al *(running from Jamie, grabs a lunch bag and threatens, in a teasing way, to throw it):* Try and stop me. *(wads up bag and throws it)*

River *(offstage):* Incoming trash.

Jamie *(looking puzzled):* What on earth? Did you guys hear that?

Skip: Hear what?

Jamie: A voice.

Al: Whose voice?

Jamie: I don't know. Just a voice. It said, "Incoming trash."

Skip: Sure, Jamie, and next you'll be saying the river was talking to us.

Jamie: No, really, I heard...

Ian: Well, it doesn't matter. At least you were trying to stop Al from trashing my special spot.

Al: What's your problem, Ian?

Ian: My problem is people like you who don't care.

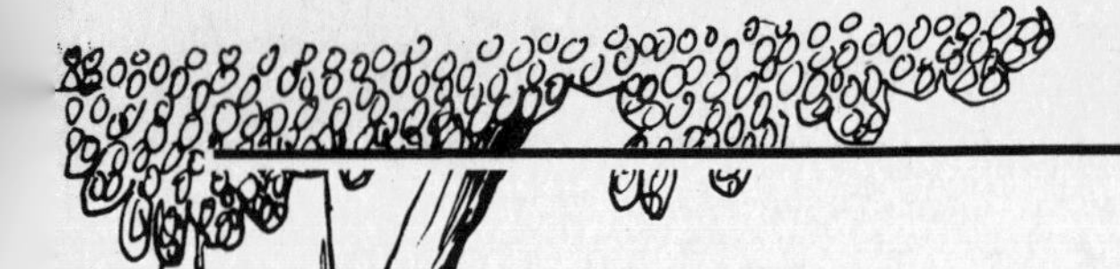

Al *(nose to nose with Ian):* Want to make something of it?

Phyllis: Hey, guys, cool it. We came on this hike for fun, not to argue.

Ian: You're right, Phyllis. I'm going up top to watch the nest. Maybe an eagle will come.

Skip: Not a chance, buddy, but I'll come watch with you anyway. *(climbs up to the platform with Ian)*

Al: Well, I haven't finished eating. *(sits down, gets more food out of his day pack and starts to eat)*

Jamie: Why am I not surprised? Hey, Phyllis. Let's lie down on the moss and watch the clouds through the treetops.

Phyllis *(lying down on the moss):* Sounds perfect.

Scene II The Awakening

(During Al's next lines, Ian and Skip pantomime watching the nest and talking to each other. Phyllis and Jamie point to the sky and pantomime talk. Eventually they all appear to doze off.)

Al: Now, for some serious eating. *(taking things out of lunch bag and reacting to each item)* Peanut butter sandwich, carrot sticks, grapes. Where's the good stuff? Oh, no. Here it is. Mom's required apple. *(looks around to see who might be watching and then tosses the apple into the forest)* They'll never know.

(Special Effect: rustling sounds)

Forest *(whispering):* Where does it come from?

Jamie *(sits up):* Phyllis. . .did you hear that?

Phyllis *(sits up):* What?

Jamie: Oh, nothing. *(lies down again)*

Al *(still looking through the bag):* There's got to be at least some trail mix in here. Ah, at last. Chocolate. *(unwrapping a candy bar)* Now, I'll be an "equal opportunity" trasher. Throw the foil wrapper into the river *(toss)* and the paper wrapper into the bushes. *(toss)*

(Special Effect: louder rustling sounds with running water sounds added)

River and Forest: Where does it come from? Where does it go?

Jamie: You had to have heard that, Phyllis.

Phyllis: What are you talking about?

Ian *(sits up):* I think I heard it, Jamie. Sort of a murmuring sound.

Jamie: It was more than just murmuring. I heard voices.

All Natural Resources *(coming onto the stage from all directions, chanting louder and louder):* Where does it come from? Where does it go? *(Introduction to the song begins as they are chanting.)*

SONG: "Where Does It Come From?" (*Natural Resources, with Jamie and Ian joining in on verses 2 and 3*)

(During this song there is a lot of movement and dance by the Natural Resources and some by Jamie and Ian.)

Jamie: Did you hear that? Those were Natural Resources singing to us.

Ian: More than that. They were asking us to think.

Al: That does it! We're out in the woods, and you two break into a song-and-dance about puppy chow and kitchen sinks. And then you say the Natural Resources are singing to you. Are you nuts?

Jamie: But Al, can't you see them?

Phyllis *(interrupting):* See who, Jamie?

Jamie: Well. . .

Ian: It's sort of hard to explain.

Skip: I'll bet, since there's nothing to see.

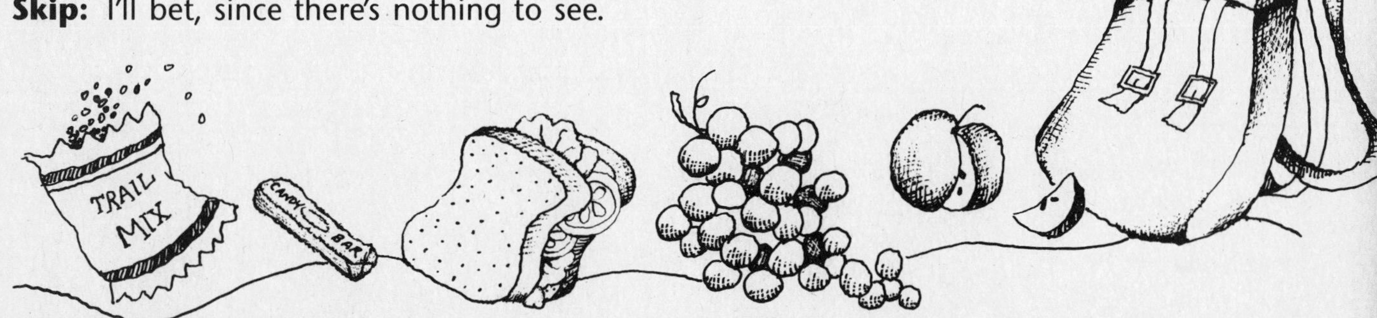

Air 1: Save your breath, Jamie and Ian.

Animal 1: Yeah. They can't see us...

Fossil Fuel 1: ...or hear us.

Ian: But, how come we can and they can't?

Air 2: Because you're Earth Kids...

Air 3: ...and they're not.

Ian: What do you mean, we're Earth Kids and they're not?

Jamie: Yeah. They're not from Mars, you know.

Al: Now, I've heard everything. What on earth are you two doing talking to the air?

Jamie: That's exactly what we are doing. Talking to the air...

Ian: ...and the river and the forest and...

Jamie: It's all the Natural Resources. They're talking to us.

All Natural Resources: We've been talking for years, but hardly anybody has paid attention.

Al: Look, Sis, I've seen you do some pretty strange things, but this takes the cake. You've got gumballs where your brain should be.

Phyllis: Now, wait a second, Al. Don't be so hard on her. In a way, I think I know what she and Ian are saying. The Natural Resources *have* been talking to us, in their own way, for years but we just haven't been paying attention.

(All Natural Resources improvise talk, agreement, milling around, etc.)

Phyllis *(leaping on to a tree stump):* Just think about it. The air has been telling us for years to stop emissions from cars but it wasn't until it started to make us sick that we paid any attention.

Air 1 *(coming closer to Phyllis):* We may have another Earth Kid in the making.

Skip: Yeah, and what about that stagnant stream at the back of the school? It looks like tar.

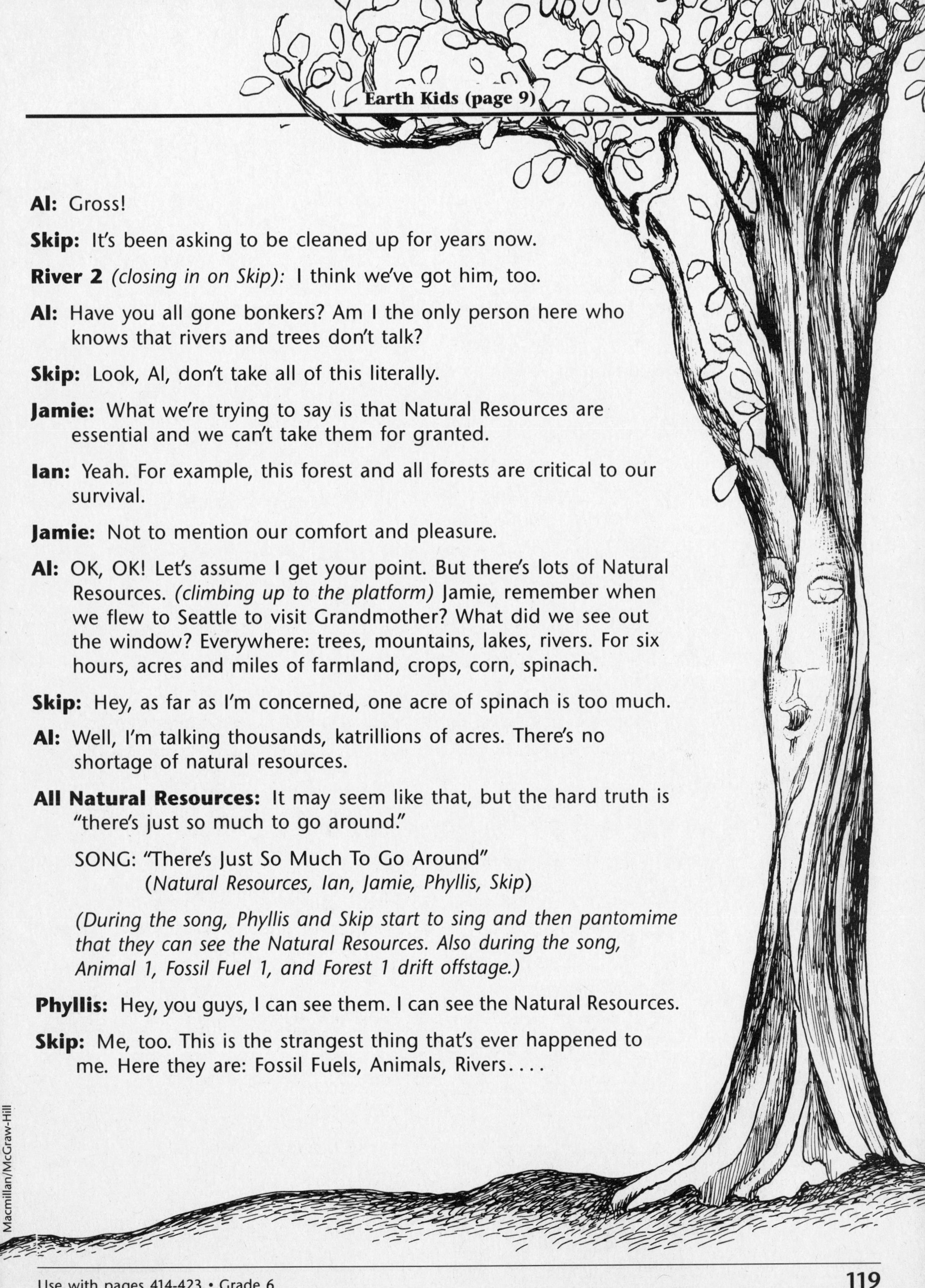

Al: Gross!

Skip: It's been asking to be cleaned up for years now.

River 2 *(closing in on Skip):* I think we've got him, too.

Al: Have you all gone bonkers? Am I the only person here who knows that rivers and trees don't talk?

Skip: Look, Al, don't take all of this literally.

Jamie: What we're trying to say is that Natural Resources are essential and we can't take them for granted.

Ian: Yeah. For example, this forest and all forests are critical to our survival.

Jamie: Not to mention our comfort and pleasure.

Al: OK, OK! Let's assume I get your point. But there's lots of Natural Resources. *(climbing up to the platform)* Jamie, remember when we flew to Seattle to visit Grandmother? What did we see out the window? Everywhere: trees, mountains, lakes, rivers. For six hours, acres and miles of farmland, crops, corn, spinach.

Skip: Hey, as far as I'm concerned, one acre of spinach is too much.

Al: Well, I'm talking thousands, katrillions of acres. There's no shortage of natural resources.

All Natural Resources: It may seem like that, but the hard truth is "there's just so much to go around."

SONG: "There's Just So Much To Go Around"
(*Natural Resources, Ian, Jamie, Phyllis, Skip*)

(During the song, Phyllis and Skip start to sing and then pantomime that they can see the Natural Resources. Also during the song, Animal 1, Fossil Fuel 1, and Forest 1 drift offstage.)

Phyllis: Hey, you guys, I can see them. I can see the Natural Resources.

Skip: Me, too. This is the strangest thing that's ever happened to me. Here they are: Fossil Fuels, Animals, Rivers. . . .

Ian: ...and can you see how yucky they're looking?

Skip: Yeah.

Jamie: Hey, gang. Something is wrong. Something is missing.

Ian: You're right, Jamie. Some of the Natural Resources disappeared during the song.

Phyllis: They must be around here somewhere.

Jamie: I think there were more animals.

Ian: Yeah, the eagle is gone, and we're definitely missing a forest.

Skip *(to Fossil Fuel 2):* Uh, Fossil Fuel. Are some of you missing?

Fossil Fuel 2: Yup. Used up.

Phyllis: Here come some more hikers. Maybe they saw them.

(Hikers enter.)

Phyllis: Hey, you guys. Did you see a Fossil Fuel or a Forest go by?

New Kid 1: No, we're looking for them ourselves.

Al: Oh, no! Tell me this isn't happening. This is just a bad dream. I am not seeing strangers who also talk to Natural Resources.

New Kid 2 *(pointing to Fossil Fuel onstage):* Look! There's some.

Skip: They're ours.

New Kid 1: Well, you're just going to have to share.

Phyllis: There may not be enough.

Jamie *(sitting on the tree stump and putting her head in her hands):* Hey, could we take a walk or something? I'm not feeling very well.

Al: I'm not surprised. It's all this craziness. *(kneels down to pantomime talk with her)*

Animal 2 *(to River 2):* I wonder if the disappearance of the Natural Resources is affecting her.

Ian: What do you mean?

River 2: Well...*(confers privately with other Natural Resources before continuing)* she very well might be an Eco-Sensor.

Ian: An Eco-Sensor?

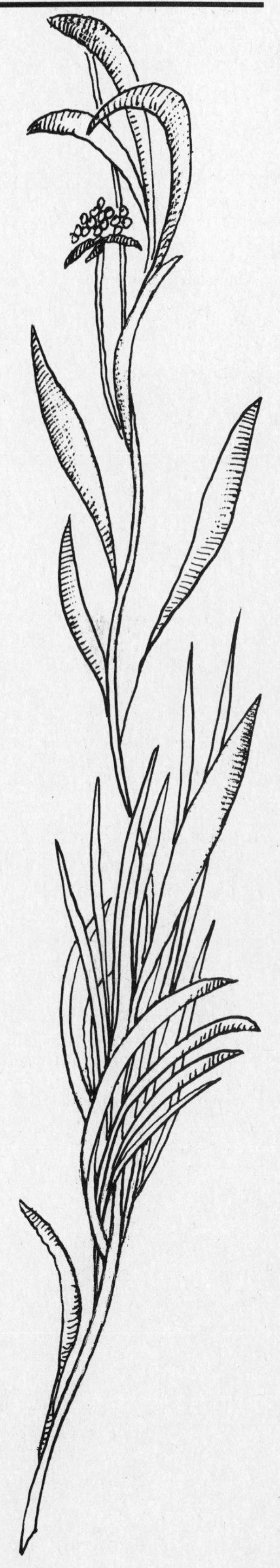

Air 3: Yeah. Have you ever heard about the "Canary in a Coal Mine"?

Kids *(shake their heads no):* No.

New Kid 2: What is it?

Air 2: Well, in the olden days, they used to lower a canary in a cage into a coal mine to see if there was a gas leak that could endanger the miners.

Air 1: The canaries were a lot more sensitive to changes in the environment than were people.

Air 3: They acted like early-warning systems.

Phyllis: What happened to the canary?

Animal 3: Let's just say they didn't need to clean out the cage anymore.

Ian: So, if Eco-Sensors are like those canaries, that means they're very sensitive.

Animal 3: Precisely. They are born to be an early-warning system to the rest of you.

Forest 2: To let you know when the Eco-System is in trouble.

Forest 1: You know, Ian, you're probably an Eco-Sensor, too.

Ian: Really?

Forest 2: Yup, you and your Grandfather.

River: The two of you have been sensitive to the needs of the environment for a long time. . .

Animal 3: . . .and you've acted on it.

Al *(leaving Jamie):* Hey, kids. Why don't we go down to the river for a while. Jamie really isn't feeling very well, and I think it might be better for her not to have all this Eco-talk going on.

Phyllis: You're probably right, Al. You all head on down. I'll catch up after I tell Jamie where we're going. *(goes over to Jamie and pantomimes a short talk)*

(All kids exit stage left, talking about the river, what has happened that afternoon, and what it all means.)

(Jamie is alone on the stage with the Natural Resources, who have assembled into their respective groups.)

Scene III The Problem

Jamie: Thank goodness they've all gone for awhile. Now I can talk with you alone.

Animal 5: What do you want to talk about, Jamie?

Jamie: Eco-Sensors. I overheard you say I was one.

Forest 3: You are—and a very sensitive one, too.

Jamie: Does that mean...does that mean I'm going to die like the canary in the coal mine?

Forest 4: Well, no. But...

Forest 5 *(backing off the stage and disappearing while speaking these lines):* You won't die from your sensitivity, Jamie, but you will feel the threat to the environment in a very real and personal way, personal way...personal way...

Jamie: Wait! Where are you going? *(to Forest 3)* Where did she go?

Forest 2: She disappeared...forever. Cut down.

Jamie *(half fainting):* Ohhhh....

Animal 3: That happens to the forests all the time.

Forest 3: Fifty acres of rain forest disappear every minute.

Jamie: Every minute?

Forest 4: That's right. And with it go the plants that could make medicine...

Animal 4: ...and habitat for endangered animal species...

Forest 2: ...and our roots to hold the soil in place to grow food...

Forest 3 *(disappearing down the center aisle and through the audience while speaking these lines):* ...and our leaves to make the oxygen you breathe...

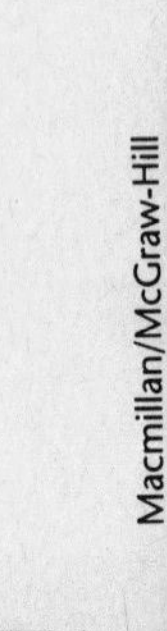

All Natural Resources: . . .breathe. . .breathe. . . .

Jamie *(running after Forest 3 down the center aisle):* Stop! Come back! We need you.

Ian *(entering from stage left):* Are you all right, Jamie?

Jamie: No, I'm not. I feel awful.

Ian: I do, too, and I'm not sure why.

Jamie: It's the forests, they're disappearing.

SONG: "Please, Don't Cut Down the Trees"
(*Jamie and Ian*)

(*Jamie sinks down on the tree stump.)*

Al *(entering from stage left and going to Ian):* There you are. How's Jamie?

Ian: Well, she's been better.

Al: Aw, come on. She's just faking to get attention.

Ian: Al! Would you cut out the overworked big-brother routine? This is your sister we're talking about, and I'm telling you something is not right here.

Al: OK, OK. It's just that. . .

Skip *(arriving from stage left with Phyllis and the New Kids*): Hey, gang. We're back.

Ian: Kids, we've got a real situation on our hands. I can feel it somewhat, but Jamie is really tuned in to it.

Phyllis: Well, what does all this mean?

Jamie: Here. Sit down. Let me explain what I know, and let the Natural Resources tell you what you need to hear.

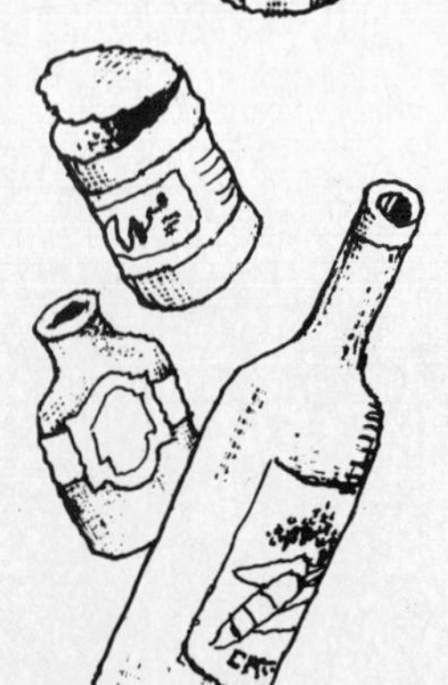

SCENE IV The Solution

(All the kids improvise lines at the same time as they sit on the ground around Jamie, who is still on the stump.)

Jamie: What I know is, we are not listening to what our world is telling us every day about the balance of nature.

Ian: And it's not just us who aren't listening. It's people all around the world.

Jamie: Our Natural Resources are being ruined or wasted at an alarming rate, and when that happens I really feel it.

Al: Sis, I'm sorry. I didn't know. I don't really want the world to lose its resources.

(Special Effects: sounds of forest, animals, air, and river)

Al: What was that?

Jamie: Al! You heard it! That was the Natural Resources reacting to your comment.

Al: It's real! You weren't just making it up.

Skip: But, Jamie, what on earth are we supposed to do about this?

All Natural Resources: We'll tell you.

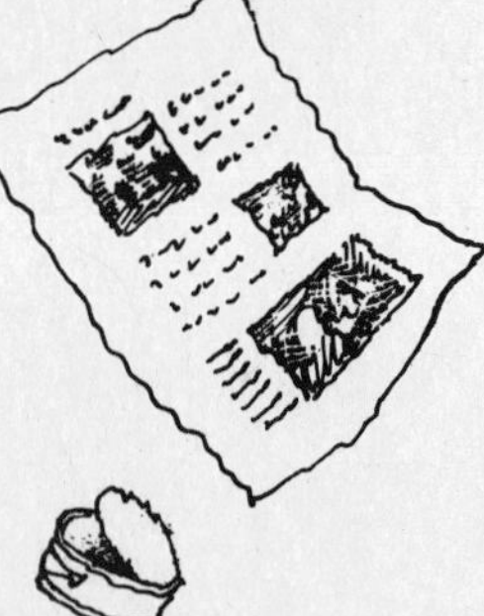

Fossil Fuel 2: For a start, try to avoid products that are used once and then thrown away.

Fossil Fuel 3: Instead of a styrofoam cup, use a glass.

Forest 4: Tell your parents to shop for products that have less packaging.

Forest 2: Carry a string bag to the store to bring groceries home in.

Air 1: . . .and, most of all, recycle.

Al: But recycling is a bother.

Animal 4: It doesn't have to be. If you and your friends band together to make it a project, it can be fun.

Animal 5: And think of the rewards.

Skip: You mean we'll get to win something?

Animal 3: Yes, you'll win a future of health, beauty, and plenty.

Al: I was hoping for a new cartridge for my video game, but okay. Where do we start?

Fossil Fuel 4: Actually, it's already started. When you use us *(indicating all the Natural Resources)* to make bottles, cans, and other packaging, a circle has begun.

Fossil Fuel 5: The trick is to continue and complete the circle.

Forest 4: Don't let the circle be broken by tossing away what can be used again.

SONG: "Keep the Circle Going 'Round"
(*Entire Cast*)

Air *(coughing and slowly exiting):* Keep the circle...the circle...circle....

Skip: What's wrong with them?

Forest: They're sick, can't you see?

Skip: Don't jump down my throat! I was just showing concern.

Air: Concern without action won't do any good.

Phyllis: Let's be practical here. What can the actions of a bunch of kids...

Jamie: ...Earth Kids...

Phyllis: OK, Earth Kids. What can a bunch of Earth Kids do?

Jamie *(as if in a trance):* We can do a lot. We've just got to believe in ourselves. Really. I can see it now....

SONG: "I Can See a Rainbow"
(*Jamie*)

(Special Effects: sounds of river, air, animals, and forest. At the conclusion of the song, all the Natural Resources start to slowly disappear, walking backwards.)

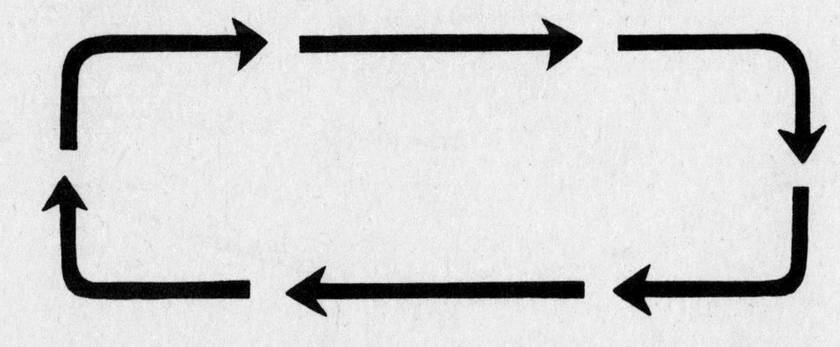

Jamie: I have to go now. I don't feel so well.

Al *(grabbing her hand):* No, Jamie. What are you doing? Why do you look so strange? *(calling out)* Somebody help me!

(All kids walk slowly, as if in a trance, and settle down in the places they were when they fell asleep.)

Al *(desperately, to Air):* What can I do?

Air: I don't know. It may be too late for her.

River 1: A lot of damage has been done.

River 2: Some reversible. . . .

Fossil Fuel: Some not so easy to reverse. For some it's just too late. . . .

Al: It's not too late. It's not too late. *(pulling harder on her arm)* Jamie, stay here. You'll be alright. *(looking at Air)* Do something!

Air: I'm sorry. We're just innocent bystanders. . . innocent victims.

Animal 2: You're the one that can make a difference.

Forest: You and the other Earth Kids.

Air: Earth Kids.

All Natural Resources: Earth Kids. . . Earth Kids. . . .

Al *(overcome with emotion):* Then we'll be Earth Kids. *(sinking into his sleeping position along with Jamie)* We'll be Earth Kids.

SCENE V The Awakening

(All is quiet except for the sounds of the forest, birds, rustling leaves, the wind, and water.)

Ian *(standing up on the platform and stretching):* Oh, my gosh. We all fell asleep. Hey, you guys. Wake up!

Skip *(sitting up):* Huh? What? Where am I?

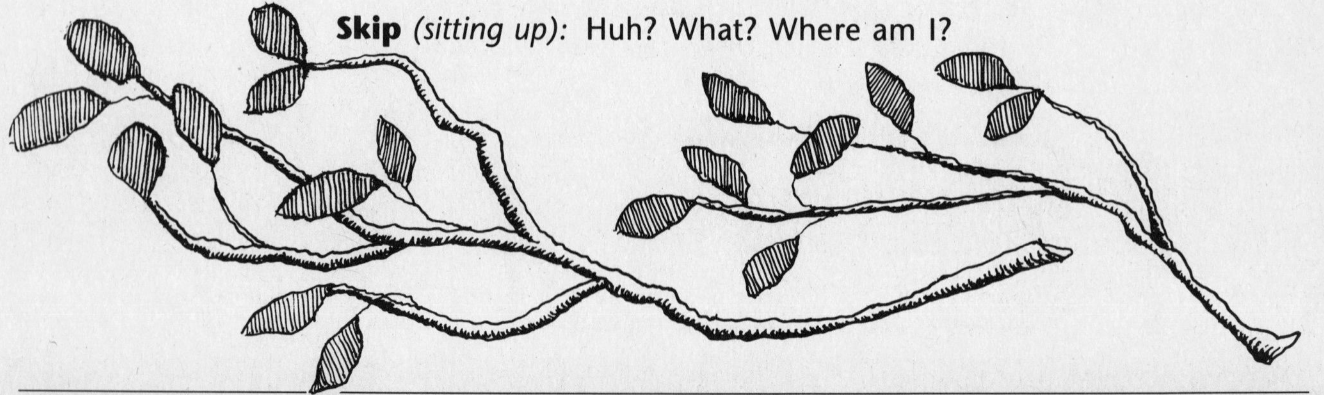

Ian: You're up in the maple tree.

Phyllis *(shaking Jamie):* Jamie, wake up. We all fell asleep looking at the sky.

Jamie: Oh, Phyllis. *(rolls over and looks around)* What are you doing here?

Phyllis: Jamie, don't you remember. We all went hiking together?

Jamie *(sitting up quickly):* Oh, yeah. We must have fallen asleep. And would you look at my brother?

Jamie *(shaking Al):* Al, wake up. Wake up!

Al *(groggily):* Huh? *(coming to his senses)* Oh, Jamie. You're here. You're alright.

Jamie: Of course, I'm alright. What are you talking about?

Al: Well, you were fading away and...

Ian: Say, what are you talking about anyway?

Al: Oh, it must have been a dream. Yeah, that's it. It was a dream.

Skip *(looking at his watch):* Do you have any idea how late it is?

Ian: Well, it's not early, that's for sure. We'd better be heading out.

Al: Say, guys. How about we do what Ian and his Grandad always do—you know, carry trash out of the forest?

Jamie *(amazed):* Hello! Is that my brother talking?

Al: Yeah, seriously. Let's clean up this place a bit before we go.

Phyllis: ...and leave it better than when we came.

Ian: Works for me. *(starts to pick up refuse and others join him)*

Al: Great. We'll be sort of...Earth Kids.

Jamie: Earth Kids?

Skip: What's that? A new band?

Al: Yeah. . . sort of. A band of kids who care about the earth. You know, all that ecological stuff that Jamie talks about.

Ian: Boy, you should take a nap in the woods more often. You must have had some dream.

Al: Actually, I had an amazing dream. I'll have to tell you about it sometime.

Jamie: Well, I had a fantastic dream, too. All about pollution. . .

Phyllis: . . .and recycling?

Ian: . . .and what we can do to help solve ecological problems?

Al: Wait a second. We couldn't have all had the same dream.

(During the following lines, all the rest of the kids return to the stage.)

Jamie: I don't know, Al, but I like the sound of what you are saying a lot.

Al: So do I. We're going to work at this Earth Kids Band—and you, sister, can be the leader.

Jamie: You bet.

SONG; "Here Come the Earth Kids"
(*Entire Cast*)

(At the end of the song, as the cast is marching out into the audience, the Natural Resources come onto the stage.)

All Natural Resources: Way to go, Earth Kids!

Al: Stop. Stop, everyone. Did you hear something?

All Natural Resources: Way to go, Earth Kids.

All Kids: Whoa. Let's go for it!

(The music begins again as the cast sings its way out of the auditorium.)

THE END

Student ______________________________ Date ____________

Portfolio Evaluation Form

Directions: For each student, review the contents of the portfolio and assign a score of 1–4 for each criterion listed below. Determine a summary score for the entire portfolio, based on Criteria 1–12 (or more).

CONTENTS	**Needs to Improve**	**Fair**	**Good**	**Excellent**
1. **Completeness.** Meets all requirements.	1	2	3	4
2. **Variety.** Includes a variety of pieces.	1	2	3	4
3. **Organization.** Shows clear organizational plan.	1	2	3	4
4. **Volume.** Includes sufficient amount of work.	1	2	3	4
5. **Focus/Purpose.** Meets intended purposes.	1	2	3	4
ATTRIBUTES				
6. **Effort.** Demonstrates concerted effort.	1	2	3	4
7. **Quality.** Illustrates appropriate level of quality.	1	2	3	4
8. **Creativity.** Shows imagination and creative ideas.	1	2	3	4
9. **Risk-Taking.** Takes risks in creating/choosing works that go beyond minimum expectations.	1	2	3	4
10. **Growth.** Shows improvement.	1	2	3	4
11. **Reflection.** Shows signs of personal reflection.	1	2	3	4
12. **Self-Evaluation.** Shows awareness of strengths and weaknesses.	1	2	3	4
THINGS YOU'D LIKE TO ADD				
13. ______________________	1	2	3	4
14. ______________________	1	2	3	4
15. ______________________	1	2	3	4
SUMMARY SCORE				
Meets the requirements of program goals.	1	2	3	4

COMMENTS

Name ____________________

RESOURCE MASTER TA•2 Tools for Assessment

Student Assessment Cards

Directions: Have students complete one or more of these cards as an attachment for each item chosen for their portfolios.

Name of piece ____________________ Date __________

My description of this piece

Name of piece ____________________ Date __________

Why I like this piece

How I might change this piece

Name of piece ____________________ Date __________

What I learned from doing this

Name ______________________________ Date ____________

Interest Inventory

Put a check beside as many answers as you like.

1. I like to. . .

________ listen to music	________ move to music
________ play music	________ compose music
________ sing songs	________ perform for others

2. Types of music I like are. . .

____

____

____

3. I'd like to know more about. . .

4. Here's an idea I'd like to try in music. . .

Name ____________________ Date __________

RESOURCE MASTER TA•4 Tools for Assessment

Self-Assessment Form

What I can do well	What I would like to do better
in listening	
in playing music	
in singing	
in moving to music	
in composing music	
in performing for others	

I'd like you to know. . .

Name ______________________________ Grade ____________

Music Log

Date	Title	What I Thought About It

Answer Key

Resource Master 1•2, Page 2

1. trombone, brass
2. timpani, percussion
3. flute, woodwind
4. cello, string
5. trumpet, brass
6. clarinet, woodwind
7. violin, string
8. gong, percussion

Resource Master 1•3, Pages 3–4

Resource Master 1•5, Page 6

order of notes: whole note, half note, quarter note, eighth note

1. a.	**5.** a.	**9.** b.	**13.** a.
2. a.	**6.** a.	**10.** a.	**14.** a.
3. b.	**7.** b.	**11.** a.	**15.** b.
4. a.	**8.** b.	**12.** b.	**16.** a.

Resource Master 1•6, Pages 7-8

1. 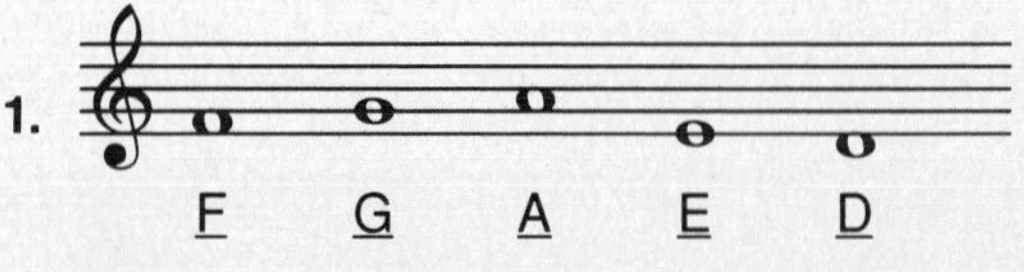
F G A E D

2. 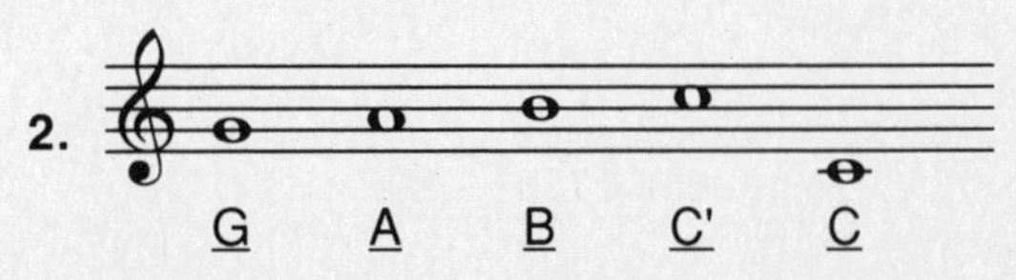
G A B C' C

3. 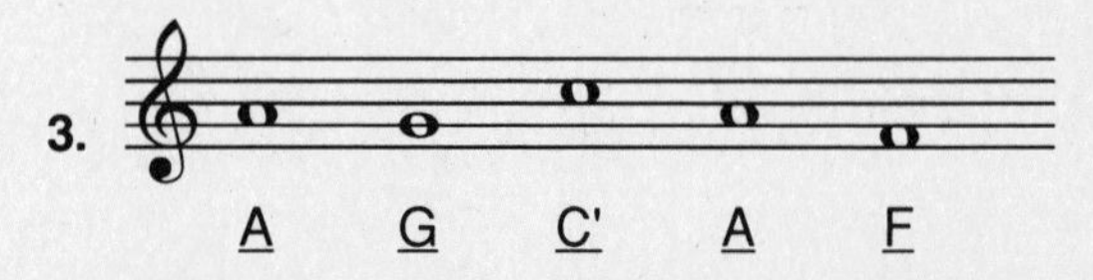
A G C' A F

4. 
E D C F G

5. 
G F D E A

6. 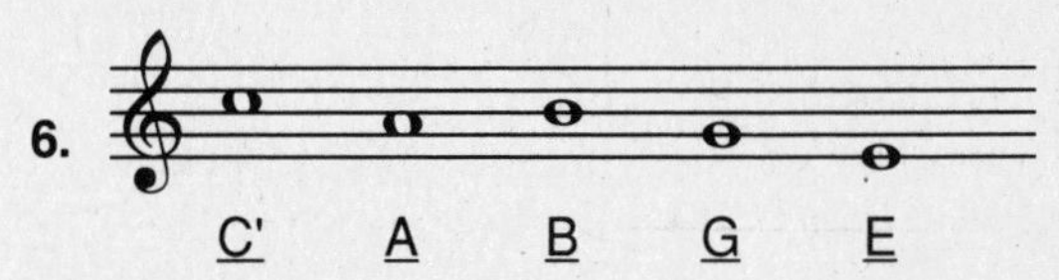
C' A B G E

7. an empty case
8. fingerprints
9. a ransom note
10. pawnshop
11. borrowed
12. repairs

Resource Master 1•7, Page 9

1. *do ti, la, so,*
   1 7, 6, 5,
2. *do so do ti,*
   1 5 1 7,
3. *do ti, do mi*
   1 7, 1 3
4. *do re ti, do*
   1 2 7, 1
5. *do so, ti, do*
   1 5, 7, 1
6. *do ti, la, do*
   1 7, 6, 1

Resource Master 1•8, Page 10

1. b.	**6.** e.	**11.** i.	**16.** l.
2. h.	**7.** o.	**12.** n.	**17.** m.
3. k.	**8.** b.	**13.** b.	**18.** h.
4. b.	**9.** a.	**14.** j.	**19.** f.
5. d.	**10.** g.	**15.** p.	**20.** c.

Resource Master 1•10, Page 13

Assessment A

1. a **2.** a **3.** c **4.** c

Assessment B

1. c **2.** b **3.** d **4.** d

Resource Master 2•3, Page 19

C major scale: C D E F G A B C'

Resource Master 2•4, Pages 20–21

1. **a.** FACE **c.** CAGE
   b. BEG
2. Possible answers: FACE, DEED, BEAD, FEED, BAG, BAD, CAB, FAD, DAD, AD, A, BE, BEE, BEEF, BEG, CAD, CAFE, CAGE, DAB, DEAF, EGG, FED, GAG, GAB, GAGE, BAGGAGE, CABBAGE, AGE

Resource Master 2•5, Page 22

Assessment A

1. c **2.** d **3.** a **4.** b **5.** b **6.** a

Assessment B

1. b **2.** b **3.** b **4.** a **5.** a. **6.** b

Answer Key

Resource Master 3•1, Pages 23–24

(All answers are rounded to the nearest tenth.)

E♭—304.0	G♯—404.9
E—321.9	A—428.8
F—340.9	B♭—454.1
F♯—361.0	B—480.9
G—382.3	C'—509.3

Resource Master 3•5, Page 41

Students should discover that the longer the stick (the vibrating part), the lower the pitch.

Resource Master 3•7, Page 43

Assessment A

1. c **2.** b **3.** b **4.** a

Assessment B

1. a **2.** d **3.** a **4.** b

Resource Master 4•6, Page 51

Assessment A

1. b **2.** a **3.** b **4.** c

Assessment B

1. a **2.** b **3.** d **4.** d

Resource Master 5•1, Page 54

1. soprano; bass
2. tenor
3. Answers will vary.

Resource Master 5•6, Page 63

Rinuccio: medium fast; medium loud; bright; marcato; tenor
Lauretta: slow; medium soft; floating; legato; soprano

Resource Master 5•8, Page 72

Assessment A

1. a **2.** d **3.** a **4.** b

Assessment B

1. c **2.** c **3.** a **4.** a

Resource Master 6•1, Page 73

1.			F	O	R	D						
2.				M	A	R	C	O	N	I		
3.			R	A	G							
4.		S	C	O	T	T						
5.	B	E	R	L	I	N						
6.				A	M	E	N	D	M	E	N	T
7.				A	E	R	O	P	L	A	N	E

Challenge: "Palm Leaf Rag," "Alexander's Ragtime Band"

Resource Master 6•2, Page 74

Events: stock-market crash; Russian Revolution ends; discovery of penicillin; Amelia Earhart flies across Atlantic; *Running Wild* popularizes the Charleston; invention of television

Challenge: "Royal Garden Blues"

Resource Master 6•3, Page 75

1. *Grand Hotel*	**4.** WPA
2. Hitler	**5.** railroad
3. jet engine	**6.** China

Challenge: "Take the A Train," "Sing, Sing, Sing," "It Don't Mean a Thing (If It Ain't Got That Swing)"

Resource Master 6•4, Page 76

1. e. **2.** a. **3.** d. **4.** c. **5.** b.

Bonus Point: Pearl Harbor